The Regenerative Materials Movement

DISPATCHES FROM PRACTITIONERS, RESEARCHERS, AND ADVOCATES

COMPILED AND EDITED BY
THE INTERNATIONAL LIVING FUTURE INSTITUTE

Contents

THE REGENERATIVE MATERIALS MOVEMENT
DISPATCHES FROM PRACTITIONERS, RESEARCHERS, AND ADVOCATES

An Ecotone Publishing Book/2023

Ecotone Publishing is an Imprint of the International Living Future Institute

International Living Future Institute
PO Box 5874
Portland, OR
97228-5874

Author: Multiple Authors
Edited by: Juliet Grable
Compiled by: International Living Future Institute
Book and Cover Design: Johanna Björk, softfirm
Cover Image: PAE Living Building (top circle).
Photograph, Lara Swimmer courtesy of PAE Engineers

Library of Congress Control Number: 2023940392
Library of Congress Cataloging-in Publication Data

ISBN-13: 978-1-7362129-2-9 (Print version)
ISBN-13: 978-1-7362129-3-6 (ebook)

First Edition Printed in Canada on FSC-certified paper, processed Chlorine-Free, with vegetable-based ink.

Photo: Bernard Hermant/Unsplash

PART III: CLIMATE + ENVIRONMENT

CONCLUSION

SUPPLEMENTARY MATERIALS

Acknowledgements

by Michael Berrisford, Ecotone Publishing

Thinking about creating shelter, the myriad choices involved, and the impact of those choices, the phrase that comes to mind is, "It takes a village..."

It certainly applies to *The Regenerative Materials Movement* — both this specific book and the greater movement it reflects. Vibrant collaborations are underpinned by a shared vision to leverage and embrace change to make the world a better place by translating research to practice, creating models that work for all, and relentless advocacy. We drew on these practices when planning, designing, and furnishing this publication. The result is a densely rich collection of essays full of ideas about how we can — collaboratively — create buildings that are healthy, equitable, restorative, and climate-resilient.

This book project came to be as a piece of The JPB Foundation's broader support of the ILFI's ongoing work to cultivate conditions in the built environment that are socially just, culturally rich, and ecologically restorative.

We are also grateful to Mohawk Industries and Buro Happold for supporting this publication and numerous other ILFI initiatives. Their approach to leadership and the pursuit of transformational excellence in the built environment makes the world a better place.

Courtesy of The Miller Hull Partnership, LLP

The Ecotone team owes a debt of gratitude to the subject matter experts who generously contributed to the book. It's an honor to include the hard-earned working knowledge of Robin Bass, Dana Bourland, William Browning, Gina Ciganik, Terry Campbell, Don Davies, Kelly Alvarez Doran, Heather Henriksen, Kathleen Hetrick, Jeff Hurley, Carol Kwiatkowski, James Kitchin, Malisa Maynard, Alison Mears, Alex Muller, Sharon Prince, Susan Puri, Christina Rabb, Hannah Ray, Jonsara Ruth, Trent Seager, Veena Singla, Lauren Sparandara, Rebecca Stamm, Charley Stevenson, Ryan Temple, Paul Vanderford, and Wendy Vittori in this publication. It was our pleasure to work with you and learn from you all.

I am grateful for the collaborations with ILFI colleagues who lent their expertise, thoughtful input, and in some cases, their knowledgeable words. We are proud to share the expert essays from Susan Puri and Hannah Ray. Lindsay Baker's insightful perspectives, Juliet Grable's unwavering professionalism, and book designer Johanna Björk's creative verve made for a remarkable team.

To everyone, I am deeply thankful for your contributions and endlessly impressed by the balance of your kindness, steadfast dedication, purpose, and tenacity with which you swim upstream against convention toward a regenerative and equitable future. Read to learn. Learn to change. Change for the better.

Introduction

by Lindsay Baker, CEO, International Living Future Institute

The design and construction of shelter is full of choices. A community of people with different roles, areas of expertise, lived experiences, and values all come together and make a set of decisions that together create a building.

We make choices about how big the space will be, what functions it will serve, whether it will be able to rely on natural light and ventilation, or whether it will require mechanical and electrical support in those pursuits. But these are not ordinary, daily choices that most people make. The thing that makes the act of building so distinct and so important is that each choice we make has lasting impacts far beyond the moment and place in which we make it. We impact the lives of people who will experience that building for decades to come; we impact the lives of people who help construct the building; we impact the lives of people who make the materials that go into it; and we impact the communities and ecosystems around the building and around the fabrication chains that feed into it.

Today, there is perhaps no set of choices that can feel more daunting and more consequential than the choices we make around the materials that go into our buildings. Like never before, research and practice have gathered a body of knowledge on the impacts of our increasingly global supply chains of building materials, and they show that so many of the materials we use are deeply harmful to human life, biological systems, our sustained economic and community health, and so much more. Through the emergence of the transparency movement that the International Living Future Institute (ILFI) has helped to lead, we are seeing a huge influx of data and reporting activity: increasingly, product manufacturers are showing building professionals what is in their products. This is great progress. We are beginning to know what we are building our buildings with, certainly enough to understand and make better decisions about the impacts we want them to have.

However, it is also a time of overwhelming information overload. The costs to vet building materials using the data we have available (while navigating the huge gaps in that data) are way too high for most building professionals to take full advantage of the information and build in line with both their values and with societal and organizational goals. The good news is, there are many organizations working hard

Photo: Pascal Meier/Unsplash

to make materials vetting as easy and simple as possible. ILFI is proud to be doing part of that work through our Declare Label program, our Living Product Challenge program, and through the facets of our work in the Living Building Challenge and elsewhere that promote awareness, best practices and advocacy around regenerative building materials. And we are also so happy to be doing this work in coalition with so many wonderful people and organizations around the world who are pushing for change alongside us.

This book is a collection of voices from that community. Together, we are working to usher in a new era of building where the materials we use are truly regenerative. When we say "regenerative," we mean materials that are safe for our bodies and ecosystems, and which actually sequester carbon emissions from our atmosphere, create great jobs that sustain families and communities, and enable local economies and communities to thrive through local fabrication and craft.

In the pages that follow, you will hear stories of celebration noting how far we have come, explanations about where we are today and how you can get involved, and some hopes and plans for the future. We decided on

...this movement is moving fast: we have no delusions that this book will feel up-to-date and thorough even five years from now. But nonetheless, we feel that it is an important act of movement building to gather these dispatches together in one place at one time so that we can learn from each other and build solidarity and momentum.

the term "dispatches" to evoke the way it feels to us at ILFI when we look out at the industry and our movement today. With so many people and organizations pursuing various efforts to push for better building materials, improve transparency, address new threats and impacts that are poorly understood and then feed this information back to the folks who are making materials decisions every day, it can be hard to keep up with all of the activity. And we also understand that this movement is moving fast: we have no delusions that this book will feel up-to-date and thorough even five years from now. But nonetheless, we feel that it is an important act of movement building to gather these dispatches together in one place at one time so that we can learn from each other and build solidarity and momentum.

As is the tradition with our work at the Institute, we sought contributions for this book from a wide range of people in a wide variety of expertise areas. Using the three pillars of our work — Climate, Health, and Justice — we sought to represent a variety of intersecting issues that all relate to the impacts that building materials have on our world. We acknowledge that there are far more topics and voices that we didn't manage to gather in this book, but we hope that it is a good introductory primer on these intersectional topics and a helpful guide for practitioners and supporters that entices and encourages deeper examination.

In reading the contributions to this book as they came in, several themes struck me that I hope will provoke thought, and indeed, action, for the reader.

The first theme that you will glean from these pages is that there is a deep and passionate agreement that this movement can only be successful through collaboration and interconnection. For example, the designers of software tools that are being created to aid decision makers and push for a faster transition are all putting in great effort to ensure that the platforms are interoperable with each other. A great deal of our efforts involves the ever-glamorous work of sitting on committees with each other, sharing knowledge and strategy. We do not always nail it when it comes to collaboration. We start doing something without realizing that someone else is already doing it; we create something for free that someone else has created to sustain their livelihoods; we disagree on how rigorous or precautionary to be and lose trust with each other. But it is critical that we continue to show up for each other, generously work through the overlaps and disagreements, and find ways to build strength for the community. Let these pages be a reaffirmation and demonstration that we are all committed to continuing that work.

The second theme that struck me relates to the rapid emergence of voices, expertise and power in the Global South. I am particularly thankful for the contribution from our colleagues at MASS Design Group, for example, for highlighting the work they are doing in Rwanda. In their piece, the authors suggest that for architecture to become regenerative, "we need to... acknowledge that we have damaged the earth and that it needs healing." Their work is a wonderful example of how to do that outside of a colonial or imperial mindset that has been common in architecture in the past century. As I write this introductory piece, the Venice Biennale for Architecture is just opening its 18th Exhibition (the *Biennale di Venezia* is in fact a tradition that dates back to 1895, with the Architecture Exhibition having begun in 1980), and for the first time in its history, it largely focuses on the work of African and African diaspora architects. One might assume therefore that its theme is simply African architecture, but one would be incorrect. The exhibition, entitled "The Laboratory of the Future," has two "twin" themes, according to the curator, Lesley Lokko of the African Futures Institute in Accra, Ghana: "decolonization and decarbonization, providing a snapshot, a glimpse of future practices and ways of seeing and being in the world."[1] It should not be surprising to learn that these "twin" themes go together, and it is exciting to see them at the forefront of the architectural discourse. It is my hope and belief that as our movement to push for truly regenerative materials grows, we will increasingly find ourselves learning from thinkers like Lokko who are helping the world envision a fundamentally different future, one that creates space for local fabrication, local economy, local materials, and indeed, local wisdom.

A final theme I read in these pages speaks to deep considerations of justice. So many of the contributors are keenly aware that historically, the modern environmental movement has not focused enough on the impacts of environmental and health injustices on low-income communities and communities of color. In the essays that follow, you will find numerous examples of these historical failures, as well as ways in which we can reverse and correct that focus. And indeed, the authors do a brilliant job of illustrating how justice is fundamental and intersectional to the work ahead. As Dana Bourland puts it in her piece that follows, "There are tremendous openings to do better that could simultaneously promote worker health, community health, and planetary health — in one fell swoop, as I like to say — by ending the cycle of pollution inherent within our building supply system."

In this movement, we have so much work ahead, even as the future of our planet and species depends on our success. But the momentum is building; awareness is growing.I hope that the stories and essays that follow inspire you, inform you, and bring you into this conversation in new ways, so that we can build this community and usher in a new era for the building industry. It is already happening in small ways all around the world; we only need to listen, learn, raise our voices, and demand that it happens everywhere. See you out there.

1 www.labiennale.org/en/architecture/2023/18th-exhibition

How to Use this Book

by Juliet Grable, Managing Editor

Photo: Daniel Ghio/Unsplash

If you've picked up this book, you are likely concerned about how the materials and products used in buildings are affecting our health, the environment, and the creatures we share this planet with. Maybe you're far down the road of materials vetting, or perhaps you've never heard of the Red List or Life Cycle Analysis; either way, you can use this book to educate yourself and others about regenerative materials: how they're defined; who is manufacturing, vetting, and using them; and the barriers to wider understanding and adoption.

Truly regenerative materials do not come at the expense of some while benefitting others, and they do not harm health. Regenerative materials minimize or mitigate climate emissions, and they can contribute to the protection and even restoration of ecosystems. For this reason, the book is divided into three sections: Justice & Equity; Health; and Climate & the Environment. Of course, these topic headings are not mutually exclusive, and many of the essays do not fit neatly under one category or another. This is not a book that must be read

chronologically; in fact, I encourage you to start with the section or essay to which you feel particularly drawn.

But education is only the beginning. Deep into editing these essays, I began having a recurring thought: If only we could get all of these people in the same room; then we might really make rapid progress in advancing the regenerative materials economy! In a way, that is exactly what this book aims to do: by collecting essays from thought leaders across sectors — research and manufacturing; practice and policy; innovation and advocacy — *The Regenerative Materials Movement* serves as a hub, and we encourage you to take advantage of it. Reach out to each other. Forge connections. Support each other's work and organizations. Find and cultivate those areas of alignment. On our end, we will be looking at ways to use the book as a launchpad for future conversations and brainstorming sessions.

I was struck with how many thought leaders include calls to action in their essays: Take those calls to heart. Utilize platforms like DECLARE and mindful MATERIALS and Red2Green; lobby your firm to start incorporating LCA into its processes; pledge to vet, as Sharon Prince urges, a single product, even if it's just one chair. Be inspired by projects like the Rwanda Institute for Conservation Agriculture and The Rose in Minneapolis and The Nature Conservancy Headquarters in Portland. Support the manufacturers that are striving toward that ideal; be guided by research that reveals which insulation types score better on environmental justice impact. As Don Davies advises, don't wait for someone else to act first before getting involved — in a process, an organization, or a cause.

Being entrusted with editing these essays was a deeply gratifying, if humbling experience. More than one of our contributors described a personal experience that fundamentally changed their approach to materials. As should become evident with each essay you read, we have come a long way, but we have even farther to go still. I invite you to use this book as a touchstone as you forge ever forward.

Photo: Saad Salim/Unsplash

PART I:

Justice + Equity

A Bold Blueprint for a Healthier Materials Economy Starts with Equity

Gina Ciganik

A decade ago, I would have said that I had a better chance of winning the lottery than being asked to write a chapter that helps create a bold blueprint for overcoming the drawbacks of our current materials economy. The blueprint must start with a great appreciation for nature and deep understanding of our inextricable interdependence with it, and it leaves no person or place behind.

The Rose, a 90-unit apartment building in Minneapolis that set a new national standard for healthy materials and the first affordable housing project to register for the Living Building Challenge. Rendering: MSR Design

My wake-up call came in 2013, during my two decades-long career as an affordable housing developer. I considered myself a sustainability warrior, and I was part of the leading-edge effort to advance energy efficiency, water conservation, social determinants of health, and more.

By that time, I had achieved U.S. Green Building Council's LEED Gold and Platinum certified buildings. I met and exceeded Enterprise Green Communities standards. I used PassivHaus principles to improve building performance. And, I was applying these standards to projects that served formerly homeless families and youth, the workforce who were paid less than a living wage, and populations often left behind by conventional financing, market prices, and systems built for some, but not all.

As I was seeking more ambitious results, I stumbled upon the Living Building Challenge, the performance-based, innovative green building standard developed by the International Living Future Institute. The Living Building Challenge asks the question, *"What if every single act of design and construction made the world a better place?"* I decided to figure out how my buildings could make the world a better place.

The Living Building Challenge introduced me to the idea that building materials are often made with toxic chemicals. These toxics harm people and the planet at all stages of the product life cycle, and they disproportionately harm Black and Brown individuals and also children, with their small, developing bodies.

Back then, I was leading the development of a project in Minneapolis, Minnesota, called The Rose. It was the first affordable housing project to register for the Living Building Challenge. And, at 90 units and more than 140,000 square feet, it was nearly three times larger than the next-biggest registered project. Most other buildings registered in that era were small, boutique buildings — nature centers and the like — and were typically only a few thousand square feet.

> The Living Building Challenge asks the question, ***"What if every single act of design and construction made the world a better place?"*** I decided to figure out how my buildings could make the world a better place.

Admittedly, I was a bit dismayed at the high design and construction costs of inaugural Living Building Challenge projects. I believed that it was likely cost prohibitive for most real estate projects to participate, let alone affordable housing. And yet, I knew that if we did not design sustainably and regeneratively for all, rather than just for a privileged few, we would never solve the globally scaled problems we face.

Scarce resources are a key talking point of "green" initiatives, typically referring to natural resources such as water, forests, land, oil and natural gas. But money is also a scarce resource. I have found that solving problems by spending more and more money inhibits creativity and erodes equity. I knew we could use the Living Building Challenge framework innovatively and cost effectively so all could participate, opening the door for any type of project to engage and contribute to the collective whole.

We dove into vetting building materials to identify safer choices. Our team found that few manufacturers would disclose product ingredients. Those that did provided complex lists of chemicals I could barely pronounce, let alone understand whether they were safe or had the potential to cause diseases and environmental harm. It was dizzying. I longed for simple, science-based guidance that could help me make decisions I could trust.

I thought I knew a thing or two about building products because I was versed in issues like lead paint and asbestos abatement. I used low-VOC (Volatile Organic Compound) paint and had already jettisoned the use of carpet in dwelling units, mostly out of concern for hygiene

Architect Paul Mellblom and Gina Ciganik, then with affordable housing nonprofit Aeon, inspects a soy-based floor material that is fully recyclable. July 2015, *Star Tribune*, photo by Jim Buchta.

and allergens that could aggravate asthma. What else was there to know?

A lot, as it turned out. I will never forget the day that Rhys MacPherson, the project architect from MSR Design, told me that the "luxury" vinyl tile (LVT), a plastic flooring product with a fake wood appearance that I regularly selected and was ubiquitous in real estate, contained chemicals called phthalates which soften plastic to increase its flexibility. Phthalates can leach out of the product and into the surrounding environment and our bodies and have the potential to damage the liver, kidneys, lungs, and reproductive system. The federal government had long banned the use of phthalates in kids' toys because studies showed that exposure to phthalates is associated with adverse impacts on neurodevelopment, including lower IQ, problems with attention and hyperactivity, and poorer social communication. Wait, what? This class of chemicals could not be in a child's rattle, but they were allowed in the 1,000 square feet of apartment flooring where a child would crawl across it every day? I didn't understand why phthalates were not banned for use in everything.

I also learned that a lot of vinyl flooring products, or their component parts, are manufactured along the Mississippi River in a place infamously called Cancer Alley, Louisiana. It earned its grim nickname because of the numerous product manufacturing facilities and chemical factories that have polluted this region. The onslaught of pollution has elevated the incidence of cancer and other diseases among people living in the "fenceline" communities abutting these industrial areas.

MARKET POWER: COLLECTIVE ADVOCACY WORKS

In 2015, Healthy Building Network and the organization's partners convinced several major retailers to ban phthalate-containing vinyl flooring from their inventories. Although there is no governmental restriction on the use of phthalates in flooring or many other products, since retailers made that commitment, tens of millions of pounds of phthalates have been eliminated from use in flooring in the United States each year. This result goes to show that change can happen regardless of whether governmental regulation exists. In fact, more often than not, governmental regulation follows market shifts.

The demographics of these areas frequently have higher percentages of people of color, lower-income households, and children than the average city in the United States. The environmental injustices and harms inflicted upon these communities are a direct result of the demand for and purchase of those products. Residents in these communities bear the burden, paying with their health. Honestly, I had never given much thought to the human and environmental impacts along the building product supply chain that made the materials that arrived on my project sites. I do now.

To add insult to injury, vinyl flooring is made of a plastic called polyvinyl chloride (PVC), which is derived from fossil fuels. Oh, the irony: we were committed to an electric building that ditched fossil fuels for clean energy, only to specify products that were made from fossil fuels. I learned that as we continue to electrify buildings and transportation, the fossil fuel industry has pivoted to provide the feedstock for the vast quantities of building materials and consumer goods we use every day. PVC has no real path for reuse or recycling, so its end-of-life destiny is the incinerator and/or perpetually growing landfill, where it will continue to slough off its chemical contents into the soil, water, and air — and ultimately, our bodies. Even though the use of phthalates in vinyl floors has been reduced, I now understand that vinyl has countless other issues when its full life cycle is examined.

I found that my go-to luxury vinyl tile (LVT) was not alone in its toxic life cycle problems. Product after product was found to have real negative human health, environmental, and justice impacts. Our heads have been in the sand on this topic, and our collective ignorance or indifference is undermining many of our other climate, health, and justice goals.

I'm happy to report that we did not select a vinyl floor for The Rose. The Armstrong *Striations* flooring the architect selected was found to be safer and eliminated over one ton of toxic chemicals when compared to the LVT we would have otherwise selected. Yes, you read that correctly: substituting one product in a single building removed more than one ton of chemicals out of the entire system. That is an enormous volume; however, some chemicals can affect our bodies at levels of one part per million, one part per billion, or even one part per trillion. This is especially true for small, developing fetuses. Sure, the product we selected cost about one dollar more per square foot in our development budget (though we could have decreased the cost if we had organized a few of our partners to buy a greater volume). I have found that many safer products are cost competitive and perform as needed; you just need to know what to ask for. The benefits to those who bear the real costs of chemical pollution and exposure along the supply chain — from manufacture, installation, use, and end-of-life — are priceless.

We made some good strides on The Rose in selecting safer products, but I realized that we were only able to nip at the edges of this enormous problem.

In fall 2015, just as The Rose was opening, I left real estate development to join Healthy Building Network (HBN). HBN is a nonprofit organization that conducts research on the chemicals used in products, including their manufacture. We provide education about the impacts of exposures to toxic chemicals and environmental pollution and create product guidance and solutions for healthier products that will support the shift towards a circular economy — that is, one which produces no waste, eliminates toxic chemicals, and creates the possibility for perpetual reuse.

Today, I work with some of the most talented chemists, material scientists, and other technical experts. Fascinating, as I was a terrible chemistry student. I have found that there is plenty of data and information available — so many 50-page reports filled with unpronounceable words — to make confident decisions about material selection.

Children are especially vulnerable to exposure to phthalates, which are found in everything from plastic toys to vinyl flooring. Photo: eclipse images/iStock

AN EQUITABLE BLUEPRINT

As part of this writing assignment, I was asked to select one of three issue areas that were identified as "equally urgent" — Health, Climate, Equity. My experience has shown me that these three things are not equally urgent. Equity is central to solving health and climate issues (and housing, education, and safety — the list goes on). Our legacy systems — everything from zoning laws and traffic planning to our financial systems and the college admissions process — were designed to benefit some and harm others. They purposefully or unwittingly exclude certain people and places-specifically, people of color and those who are not paid living wages (or otherwise have low incomes), and they are not designed with children in mind.

Exclusionary systems not only disproportionately harm those left out, they undermine the success of the ambitious, scaled, and necessary sustainability goals that we've set to save the planet and ourselves. We will not solve the climate crisis if solutions are not designed for all. We will not solve the health crisis if solutions are not accessible to all. We will not solve any of it if we work in silos rather than in a way that acknowledges intersectionality, recognizing a combination of factors.

Here is what I have learned along my journey that I believe will contribute to a bold, equitable blueprint for overcoming the drawbacks of our current materials economy.

1. Raise awareness: My first insight is that there is a fundamental lack of awareness or disbelief that our bodies contain chemicals and micro-particles of "stuff" not meant to be inside of us, causing disease. The reality is that we are what surrounds us. Educate yourself about science-based solutions, demand transparency and safer products, and surround yourself and others with non-toxic and natural things.

2. Act holistically, not in silos: Climate solutions will not succeed unless they include the reduction of hazardous chemicals. Most climate plans have a fatal flaw of ignoring toxic chemicals, plastics, and pollution. Decarbonization AND detoxification AND achieving environmental justice is the only way toward a healthy, abundant, and just planet.

3. Fix the flawed math: We must get the math right. When evaluating the "expense" of healthier products versus business-as-usual, a fair calculation for the latter needs to include all costs associated with their production, use, and end of life impacts. That "cheap" vinyl floor is no longer so inexpensive when the full costs of global pollution and the health burdens of people of color and low-income communities are included in the math. Externalities such as increased health care costs for those disproportionately exposed, clean-up costs of pollution, and all of the burdens of overflowing landfills and burning waste must be a part of the equation.

4. Stop over-complicating things: We make things too hard. There are simple, science-based solutions that we all can pursue to stop using the worst-in-class, "red-zone" products that are polluting our bodies and the planet.

5. Design with the most vulnerable in mind: If a product or material is safe for children, it will be safe for all people and the planet. Why would we not want to do that? If we want to solve this problem, approach product design and product selection in a manner that is safe for children at all stages of the product's life cycle. A precautionary, children-first approach will, by its nature, move us closer to justice, health, and a low-carbon economy.

Planned for San Jose, CA, The Magnolias is a 66-unit modular affordable housing project developed by First Community Housing and designed by SERA Architects. The project team collaborated with Healthy Building Network (HBN) to identify healthier material options to improve occupant health and reduce impacts on fenceline communities. Rendering: SERA Architects

What we now need is:

1. Translation of that data into simple, science-based, actionable guidance for non-chemists who are making decisions on products every day; and

2. Social science–truly understanding human beings, their motivations, workflows, barriers, fears, biases, and other idiosyncrasies so we can better influence and guide choices and behavior.

Co-creating solutions together with our audiences, in their language and in a manner that fits their needs, is the way forward.

We are doing just that with our easy-to-use red (worst) to green (best) product rankings — a tool I wished I'd had back when I was working on The Rose. We now have many partners successfully implementing this product guidance–SERA, for example, used it to inform the design of a modular affordable housing project in California called Magnolias. Who knew that my disdain for chemistry would someday become my superpower.

The United Nations projects that 2.5 trillion square feet of real estate will be added to the planet by 2060, doubling what exists on the earth today. This expansive development

Photo: Andrew Coelho/Unsplash

comes at a time when international scientists have concluded that chemical pollution (inclusive of plastics) has crossed the planetary boundary deemed safe for humanity. The scale of the built environment gives us the power to either select the path towards healing the planet or be responsible for its degradation. I know that we can come together, reimagine our work, and select the path where all people and the planet thrive because of sound decisions about our built environment.

My challenge for you is to start by eliminating those worst-in-class products ranked in the red zone.

To borrow a phrase from one of our foundations: "There is an urgent need in our world for healing: healing our planet, healing our communities, and healing ourselves in body, mind, and spirit." A bold, equitable, blueprint for a safe and circular economy, one that honors nature and is designed to protect the most vulnerable children, will position us to do just that.

There is an urgent need in our world for healing: healing our planet, healing our communities, and healing ourselves in body, mind, and spirit.

Gina Ciganik has been growing and scaling HBN's vision since assuming the CEO role in 2016. Previously she served as HBN's Senior Advisor for Housing Innovation, establishing and leading the HomeFree initiative, an expansion of HBN's healthy materials work into the affordable housing sector.

Gina is recognized as a national leader in transforming human and environmental health through strategic partnerships, innovative business practices, capacity building, and novel approaches. A champion of equity and environmental justice, Gina is an innovator with a proven track record of creating leading-edge, nationally recognized sustainable spaces where we live, work, and play.

Prior to HBN, Gina was Vice President at a Minneapolis-St. Paul area real estate developer, where she spent two decades creating thousands of healthy, high-performance affordable homes. Her efforts culminated in the construction of The Rose, a 90-unit apartment building in Minneapolis that set a new national standard for healthy materials.

Gina was named to Finance and Commerce's Top Women in Finance (2012 & 2015), and in 2021 received a Women in Sustainability Leadership Award (WSLA), one of the most prestigious awards honoring leadership in sustainability across the globe. She completed the Achieving Excellence program at Harvard University's JFK School of Government and holds a B.S degree in Housing from the University of Minnesota.

HEALTHY BUILDING NETWORK

Vision: All people and the planet thrive when the environment is free of toxic chemicals.

Mission: To advance human and environmental health by improving hazardous chemical transparency and inspiring product innovation.

Since 2000, HBN has defined the leading edge of chemical hazard transparency and created market demand and incentives for safer innovations in green chemistry and product manufacturing, resulting in healthier products and reduction of human exposures to hazardous chemicals.

We pursue our mission on three fronts: 1) research: uncovering cutting edge information about healthier products and health impacts, 2) data systems: producing software platforms that aggregate and catalog product transparency and chemical hazards, and 3) education and capacity building: fostering others' capabilities to make informed decisions. When we know better, we do better.

Our mission and work is grounded in health, equity, and environmental justice. A founding principle embedded in all of our work is accounting for the disproportionate exposures to toxic chemicals by Black, Indigenous, and other people of color – in the affordable housing sector and the legacy redlined neighborhoods and fenceline communities that abut industrial facilities. We make room at the table for voices that are regularly excluded from the conversation to shape and lead solutions.

Embodied Suffering in Our Building Materials

Sharon Prince

"Would we consider awarding a project that may have materials made with forced or child labor?" I asked, when I was on the AIA National Jury in 2017. We were evaluating a design for a girls' school in a country that is a global hotspot for child labor, and therefore had a very high likelihood of exploiting young children to make the bricks used in its very walls.

The question was met with silence.

Design for Freedom is a movement to create a radical paradigm shift and remove slavery from the built environment. Photo: Sarin Soman via Getty Images

What we know now is that nearly every project has exposure to exploitation baked into their building materials.

Nearly 28 million people around the world suffer under forced labor conditions, working in hazardous and inhumane environments to make and extract building materials. There are 160 million children in child labor conditions globally. Although modern slavery, which encompasses human trafficking and forced labor, is illegal in every country, these practices continue with impunity.

Despite the horrendous conditions faced by so many people around the world, there is no way of knowing the human cost of the materials we specify because there is no inspection process.

A country of origin and fair labor label is very often missing on the thousands of selected building materials that go into one project. Understanding the provenance of and who makes the materials such as bricks, timber, iron, and concrete that are used to build our homes, offices, schools, and stores is rarely, if ever, considered today. And yet,

Figure 1. The *Design for Freedom Report* include a list of the 12 raw and composite materials, used ubiquitously across the globe, that carry the highest risk of embedded slavery.
Source: *Verité Commodities Atlas* and the U.S. Department of Labor's *List of Goods Produced by Child Labor or Forced Labor*, Grace Farms analysis

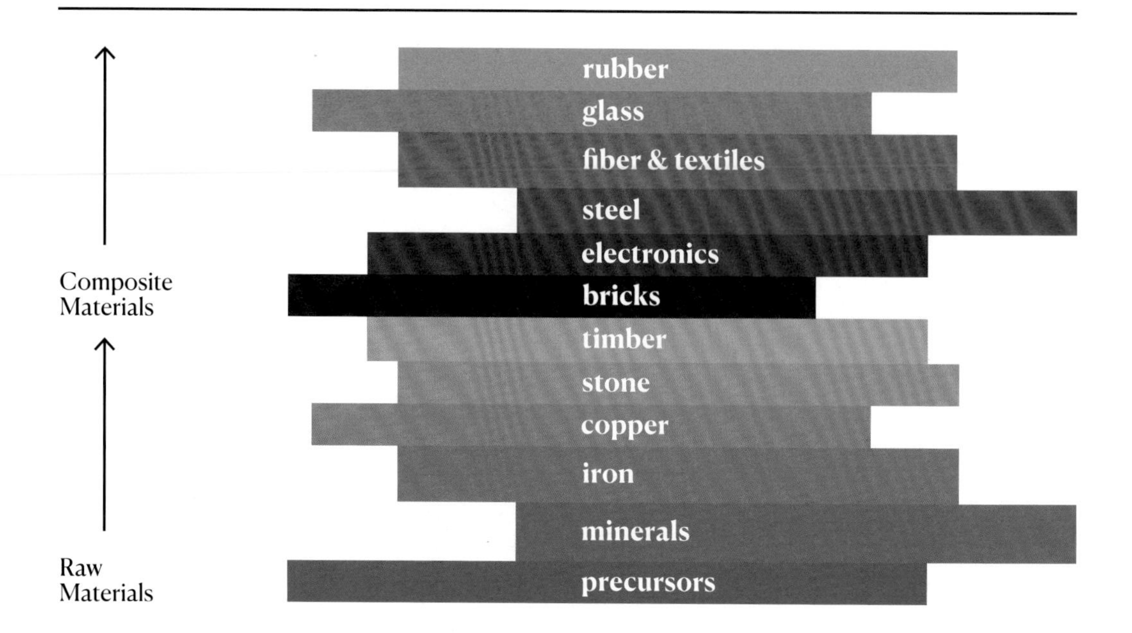

once we know about the issue of forced labor in our supply chains, we are obligated to ask these questions and take action.

The largest industrialized sector with the highest risk of modern slavery is getting a labor transparency pass. It is stunning that today there is no ethical labor inspection of the building materials supply chain, which accounts for roughly 50 percent of the building's cost. In addition, the construction sector is the single highest contributor to climate change, with the highest embodied carbon, and is also the industrial sector with the highest embodied suffering.

We at Grace Farms are working to change that. First food, then clothing was brought to the table to account for fair labor in its material supply chain. Next will be shelter.

DESIGN FOR FREEDOM

Grace Farms is a humanitarian and cultural center whose mission is to end modern slavery and create more grace and peace in our local and global communities. With our open architecture, Grace Farms breaks down barriers between people and sectors and invites conversation, curiosity, and proximities. Our advocacy to end modern slavery met our investment in architecture when we launched Design for Freedom, an initiative to create a radical paradigm shift to remove forced and child labor from the building materials supply chain. The Design for Freedom movement has brought together more than 80 global industry leaders to eliminate forced labor in the built environment. By taking a top-down approach, we can create true

Photo: zms/iStock

market transformation and build a more equitable future.

Particularly at a time when ESG (Environmental, Social, and Governance) investing has been prioritized and the green building movement has been integrated in the construction sector, the industry is primed to adopt Design for Freedom Principles - a new mandate to ensure ethical procurement and a more transparent building materials supply chain. Incorporating ESG's social responsibility standards in the built environment could better safeguard workers and create a more humane future for all. A question at the core of Design for Freedom is: *Is your building ethically sourced and forced-labor free, as well as sustainably designed?* The answer is, we do not know. Without inspection of the thousands of raw and composite materials, there is no accountability, and the most egregious social equity violation of forced and child labor proliferates.

We developed Design for Freedom with the understanding that there is a startling blind spot in terms of the entropic brutality forced upon the workers who are critical to the production of the very materials we source, even those selected using a sustainability lens. Their suffering should not be incorporated into our construction.

After two years of developing a committed working group of leaders from the architecture, engineering, and construction industries, we launched Design for Freedom in 2020 with the *Design for Freedom Report*, establishing the basis for this new

FORCED LABOR IS NEVER SUSTAINABLE

It is important to note that environmental sustainability does not hold up with forced labor. Solar panels are dependent on cheap polysilicon, and 45 percent of the global supply is sourced from China's Xinjiang Uyghur Autonomous Region, where millions are held in forced labor conditions and detained in camps. The recently enacted Uyghur Forced Labor Protection Act (UFLPA), which took effect on June 21, 2022, is a bold new type of American legislation that will have long-term impacts on how we source materials, increase supply chain transparency, and hold violators to account. This legislation prohibits importation into the United States of any goods and merchandise mined, produced, or manufactured wholly or in part in the Xinjiang Uyghur Autonomous Region of the People's Republic of China. And it is already making a difference. Between June 21 and October 25, 2022, more than 1,000 containers of solar panels worth hundreds of millions of dollars have been detained at United States ports of entry. This kind of enforcement is critical to making the long-term change to remove forced labor from the products that are used in construction.

architectural justice movement. There was no list of at-risk materials, so we researched and developed a list of 12 raw and composite materials with longstanding histories of human rights violations right in front of us. Among these are such ubiquitous building materials as steel, glass, minerals, bricks, stone, copper, and textiles. Timber, for example, is one of the world's most widely used construction materials; it is also one of the most fraught with problems. According to the United States International Trade Commission, 38 percent of wood products globally are used for construction and up to 50 percent of global illegal logging is dependent on forced labor. Imagine the difference that could be made if project teams examined the provenance of timber on its projects and took labor inputs into account. It would be transformative.

To do this work and mobilize the industry, we have brought together progressive leaders within the ecosystem of the built environment — CEOs, deans, architects, construction managers, lawyers, and government agencies. Design for Freedom is prompting architects, engineers, designers, owners, specifiers — essentially all of us, as we all influence the supply chain and are a part of the built environment — to add human rights as a fundamental criterion in building material specification and procurement. We need to envision our buildings being built without forced labor, without slavery embedded in our foundations, curtain walls, interiors, and landscapes.

TOWARDS ARCHITECTURAL JUSTICE

Practices that harm the natural environment and prioritize consumption and low-cost production are the same practices that fuel the injustices of forced and child labor. In other words, there is an inverse relationship between lower material costs — driven lower with speed and other "efficiencies" — and increased human suffering. As Dr. Harriet Harris of the Royal College of Art has noted, "More recently the term sustainability is firmly understood to encompass the ecological meaning that social sustainability is an 'ecological domain' — in other words, a form of human embeddedness in the environment. You cannot consider the environment without the people that live within it."

Social equity which prioritizes ethical material procurement is the next step in architectural justice. Minimizing the risk of embodied suffering can be achieved in parallel to the movement to minimize embodied carbon. The Design for Freedom Toolkit notes relevant sustainability certifications and standards that also include third-party fair labor audits. We also affirm that material circularity truncates the material supply chain at the extraction level, which operates at the highest risk of forced and child labor. Digital platforms that aggregate certifications and standards like mindful MATERIALS are working with us to incorporate a Design for Freedom Principles filter. Turner Construction, which represents 10 percent of the United States marketplace for construction, is going beyond the first Design for Freedom Pilot Project transparency work and aims to add Design for Freedom Principles more broadly. The United States Department of State's Overseas Building Operations, which oversees more than $13 billion in projects, has also made a trajectory shifting commitment to Design for Freedom, which will create a cascading effect in material transparency means and methods.

Embodied carbon is refreshing the conversations with manufacturing partners about their full material supply chain. Our hope is this dialogue will catalyze improvements in manufacturing processes to lower their environmental impact while simultaneously opening the door for an examination of the human rights impact, stimulating an ethical supply chain. To this end, Buro Happold engineers are leading a team within our Design for Freedom Working Group to research and add labor inputs into their BIM + embodied carbon project.

Social equity which prioritizes ethical material procurement is the next step in architectural justice.

According to the United Nations, almost one in ten of all children globally are subjected to child labor. In the least developed countries, slightly more than one in four children, ages 5 to 17, are engaged in labor that is considered detrimental to their health and development. These children work in deplorable conditions, often extracting and harvesting the very materials that go into the buildings in which we live and work. There is clearly a grave human cost when there is no supply chain inspection.

Advocating for change is not enough. We must meet this moment with action to generate real change.

This grave cost is even more urgent to address in light of a warming planet, extreme weather, and climate change, as the impacts of these crises are felt disproportionately by the most vulnerable. Climate change is forcing mass migration as crops, water sources, and farming opportunities continue to dwindle. As we note in our *Design for Freedom Report*, a migrant workforce is one of the top key risk factors for modern slavery. In June of 2022, the United Nations announced an "intolerable tide" of people displaced by climate change, noting that more than 59 million people were internally displaced in 2021, most by climate related disasters. They also added that this figure is "far higher" than those displaced by armed conflict.

We need to bring all that we can to confront these greatest of humanitarian issues. Advocating for change is not enough. We must meet this moment with action to generate real change.

Design for Freedom Pilot Projects are helping us to do just that, by providing material transparency and prioritizing ethical procurement. As of December 2022, there are five Design for Freedom Pilot Projects in the United States, the United Kingdom, and India, including the 21st Serpentine Pavilion, *Black Chapel*, by Theaster Gates, *Shadow of a Face*, a monument to Harriet Tubman by Nina Cooke John, and a new center for arts and culture by Serendipity Arts in New Delhi, India. These projects are adding to the body of knowledge while also creating tangible examples of a more humane built environment. These projects have already catalyzed positive action. We are gathering new research, testing new means and methods, and convening ethical action meetings to educate practitioners and communities about forced labor in our building materials supply chain and the agency that each of us has to address it.

Prince Zeid Ra'ad Al Hussein, former United Nations High Commissioner on Human Rights, opened the first Design for Freedom Summit at Grace Farms with me and noted that "All good revolutions start like this."

This is revolutionary work and everyone has a role to play. *Everyone has the wherewithal to inspect at least one material end to end, even one chair.*

Fair labor building materials can and will be a central driver for solving a timeless humanitarian challenge and yes, for creating a more humane future. This is a rare and promising moment to initialize transparency in an opaque, weighty marketplace. We can and must investigate the materials that we build with to create market transformation and end embedded suffering in our buildings.

Sharon Prince is the CEO and Founder of Grace Farms Foundation and leads the Design for Freedom movement to eliminate forced labor in the building materials supply chain. Prince launched Design for Freedom in 2020 with the publication of a groundbreaking report on how forced labor is embedded into the very foundations of our buildings. In 2022, at the inaugural Design for Freedom Summit, Prince released the *Design for Freedom Toolkit*, a resource that professionals can use to integrate Design for Freedom Principles into their practices. She has also mobilized more than 100 leaders of the built environment to come alongside her in this work as a part of the Design for Freedom Working Group. Prince is also a social entrepreneur who co-founded Grace Farms Foods, a premium tea and coffee certified B Corp that educates the public about the work of Grace Farms and demonstrates what the Foundation advocates for: ethical and sustainable supply chains.

Grace Farms has garnered numerous awards for contributions to architecture, environmental sustainability, and social good, including the AIA National Architecture Honor Award and the Mies Crown Hall Americas Prize. Prince's leadership and humanitarian work at Grace Farms and Design for Freedom has been widely recognized. She received the NYC Visionary Award from AIA-NY and the Center for Architecture and *Fast Company* has named her one of the Most Creative People in Business for "cleaning up construction."

GRACE FARMS

Grace Farms is a center for culture and collaboration in New Canaan, Connecticut. We bring together people across sectors to explore nature, arts, justice, community, and faith at the SANAA-designed River building on 80 acres of publicly accessible, preserved natural landscape. Our humanitarian work to end modern slavery and foster more grace and peace in our local and global communities includes leading the Design for Freedom movement to eliminate forced labor in the building materials supply chain.

Rebuilding and Reimagining an Equitable Manufacturing Future in Chicago and Beyond

Jeff Hurley

"I'm in the business of making money, not making steel."

So said David Roderick in *Steelworker Alley*, Robert Bruno's book on the culture of Ohio steelworkers. As CEO of U.S. Steel, Roderick made the decision to dismantle South Works, a manufacturing plant south of Chicago, in the early 1990s. Once viewed as the industrial center of America, Chicago saw almost 4,000 companies close and 200,000 manufacturing jobs lost in the last two decades of the 20th century (Swinney, n.d.).

Deindustrialization left jobless residents and disinvested neighborhoods in its wake. Those affected most by this loss were people of color, particularly African Americans. According to a report by the

The loss of manufacturing jobs has hollowed out communities in Chicago and other traditional manufacturing hubs. Photo: Luca Upper/Unsplash

Great Cities Institute, a third of Black workers in Chicago worked in manufacturing in the 1960s. In 2015, only 5 percent of Black workers were employed in this sector.

This decline has left behind a legacy of income inequality and economic and health disparities. Much has been written on the downward trend of manufacturing in the United States; what is often underappreciated is how destructive this downturn has been for the Black workforce. For those wondering how a 30-year life expectancy gap (Schencker, 2019) is possible between Streeterville and Englewood, two neighborhoods in Chicago separated by eight miles, the racial segregation in population and manufacturing distribution (Córdova et al., 2018) is partly to blame.

Photo: Mikita Yo/Unsplash

WHAT MANUFACTURING MEANS TO THE MIDDLE CLASS

What was once a backbone of the American economy has gradually — but steadily — seen jobs disappear and factories close. There are many culprits: globalization, automation, poor trade deals, and low domestic savings by the federal government, but the bottom line is that the United States has seen trade deficits continually increase over the last thirty years, with an annual goods deficit reaching an all-time high of $1.1 trillion in 2021 (Bureau of Economic Analysis, 2022). To put this into perspective, that's roughly the same as the Gross Domestic Product of the Netherlands, the world's 18th largest economy.

These trade deficits have resulted in the loss of over 5 million American manufacturing jobs and almost 70,000 factories (Scott et al., 2022). As manufacturing jobs have slowly dissipated, middle-class workers have transitioned to the service sector for work, where they make less money and receive lower benefits. Today, there are almost as many people working in restaurants as manufacturing, whereas in 1990 manufacturing was three times larger than the food-service industry (Thompson, 2017). In cities like Cleveland and New Orleans, a third of new jobs are in restaurants. This shift from manufacturing and construction industries into the service industry has resulted in lost wages and lost opportunities for non-college educated workers.

DISPROPORTIONATE IMPACT ON THE BLACK WORKFORCE

As manufacturing jobs in America declined, Black Americans faced a disparate impact compared to their white colleagues in the manufacturing industry. Systemic racism and oppression are part of the fabric of the nation, and this is represented within the manufacturing industry and the fallout from its decline. According to a report from the Economic Policy Institute, between 2001 and 2011, 958,000 workers of color were displaced from higher-earning manufacturing and building trade industries into lower-earning jobs in other industries.

In the 20th century, manufacturing offered many opportunities for Black workers and allowed Black families to move into the middle class. But as Black workers' proportionate share of manufacturing jobs flatlined and then suffered a 30 percent decline, there were no retraining efforts for employment, and these workers were often left behind in industrial communities with declining revenues and eroding infrastructure.

This disparity is part of a larger conversation on economic inequality and the growing gap between the wealthiest Americans and the average worker, which has reached the highest level recorded since the United States Census Bureau began tracking this information (Telford, 2019). There is a direct correlation between the increase in income equality and the decrease of worker power through participation in labor unions. Unfortunately, unionization in the manufacturing sector has been on a steady downslope for the past 20 years, declining from 15.5 percent in 2001 to 8.5 percent in 2021 (Hirsch et al., 2023). In turn, the wage advantage of workers directly employed in manufacturing has fallen from 14.7 percent in the 1980s to 10.4 percent in the 2010s, as reported by economist Lawrence Mishel (Mishel, 2018).

Photo: Obradovic/iStock

ADVANCING CLEAN TECHNOLOGY MANUFACTURING AND REBUILDING THE MIDDLE CLASS

The remedy is investing in domestic manufacturing to restore quality American jobs that are clean, safe, and fair for workers and communities. Despite the loss of jobs over recent decades, manufacturing still employs roughly one in 11 American workers, and there are opportunities for further growth in this sector that can also provide pathways into the middle class through high-skill, high-wage jobs (Scott, 2015). This can be achieved several ways:

First, by applying "Buy American" and comparable domestic content requirements on manufacturing-related policies. Supporting American-made products not only helps maintain quality jobs, it also generates economic activity and drives overall economic innovation.

Public spending should be focused on supporting domestic manufacturing jobs, not corporations that outsource production to countries with lower labor and environmental standards. Combining this with Davis-Bacon prevailing wage, project labor agreements, and high labor standards can create family-sustaining jobs that offer strong wages and benefits.

Manufacturing is great, but manufacturing that benefits the clean economy is better. Public investments and policies can play a key role in creating demand for clean technology, while also spurring domestic manufacturing and setting a high standard for jobs and community benefits. Fortunately, this is already happening.

Photo: Eric Wang/Unsplash

STEPS TOWARD AN EQUITABLE MANUFACTURING SECTOR

While the pandemic caused a loss in manufacturing employment in a majority of states, there may be light at the end of the tunnel (Henderson, 2022). The manufacturing sector has displayed stability and the possibility for growth in the pandemic's wake. There is an opportunity to uplift overlooked communities in Chicago through innovative and inclusive training programs that can create pathways for people of color into skilled manufacturing careers. The manufacturing sector has shown a capacity for growth, adding jobs at the fastest annual pace in nearly forty years (FRED Economic Data, 2023). A study by the Century Foundation found that manufacturing has more job openings than all but three sectors (health care, professional services, and finance), with two manufacturing jobs open for every hire (Córdova et al., 2018). This inability to hire enough workers is a reversal from earlier periods, when manufacturers saw greater demand for jobs than they had positions to fill.

The BlueGreen Alliance (BGA) has strived to lead reinvestment in manufacturing in order to lessen economic, racial, and environmental injustice across America. BGA unites labor unions and environmental organizations to solve today's environmental challenges in ways that create and maintain quality jobs and build a clean, prosperous, and equitable economy. BGA has recently developed a report outlining policy suggestions for enhancing career pathways and expanding job quality and opportunity for people of color. The *Solidarity for Racial Equity* platform recommends accessing opportunities through successful pre-apprenticeship programs, designing pipelines for students to transition to well-paying trade jobs by calling for stronger support of training programs at the high school level, addressing historical, systemic discrimination in labor, and creating jobs in clean energy and manufacturing that target underserved communities (Avila & Brody, 2022).

One of the main mechanisms for building career pathways is through apprenticeship, pre-apprenticeship, and other union-affiliated training programs. Registered apprenticeships are paid positions that combine on-the-job training with classroom instruction in a trade. An internal BlueGreen Alliance analysis of the Department of Labor's Registered Apprenticeship Partners Information Database System (RAPIDS) found that people of color represented 43 percent of the apprentices in union programs, compared to 33 percent in non-union programs (U.S. Department of Labor, n.d.). Pre-apprenticeship programs have become a key tool for improving diversity, ensuring workers qualify for entry into an apprenticeship program, and equipping them with the skills they need to succeed. These programs are generally designed to target certain demographics such as low-income workers, workers of color, women, and other marginalized populations.

The Inflation Reduction Act, which was signed into law in August 2022, is a significant step in the right direction. In the

Moving forward, in order to transition on an industrial scale via clean technology, the manufacturing sector needs to create a more equitable and labor-supported talent pathway and leverage the services of local organizations.

past there has been a perception that we must choose between quality jobs or a clean environment (BlueGreen Alliance, 2022). This legislation delegitimizes this false dichotomy through robust investments in both. In addition to supporting and creating good union jobs, investing in economic and racial justice programs, and strengthening domestic manufacturing, the Inflation Reduction Act allots $50 billion to the manufacturing of clean energy technologies — the largest ever such investment in United States history. This funding will create an estimated 9 million jobs over the next decade (BlueGreen Alliance, 2022). Through loans, grants, and tax credits, the law will boost clean vehicle manufacturing to bolster the electric vehicle (EV) transition and support new production in solar, wind, and battery manufacturing, all while incentivizing the use of union labor and ensuring equitable access to the jobs the Inflation Reduction Act will create.

At the same time, forward-thinking state legislation can help reinvigorate the manufacturing sector while addressing equity and greenhouse gas emission targets. In 2021, Illinois passed the Climate and Equitable Jobs Act (CEJA), which not only targets clean energy and decarbonization commitments, but combines targeted labor incentives with a desire to increase representation of Black and Latino communities, offering training to help residents in these communities land union jobs in clean energy development. CEJA will accomplish these objectives by creating "hubs" throughout Illinois to ensure equity-focused populations can participate in the clean energy sector. The program is also funding pre-apprenticeship training programs and recruiting candidates from areas identified as "environmental justice communities." Combined, CEJA and the Inflation Reduction Act will allow Illinois to reach zero-emission goals while expanding career opportunities for residents in historically underinvested communities.

THE WAY FORWARD

These are significant steps in the right direction, but for Chicago and the Midwest to equitably regain their footing in the manufacturing industry, more is needed to restore sustainable jobs that uplift the middle class and underrepresented groups. Moving forward, in order to transition on an industrial scale via clean technology, the manufacturing sector needs to create a more equitable and labor-supported talent pathway and leverage the services of local organizations. This path must be inclusive and consider the well-being of both employees and the greater community. Despite the proclamations of Mr. Roderick, there's more to manufacturing than a tunnel-vision pursuit of the financial bottom line.

REFERENCES

Avila, E. & Brody, C. (2022). ***Solidarity for racial equity.*** BlueGreen Alliance (BGA). www.bluegreenalliance.org/wp-content/uploads/2022/01/Solidarity-for-Racial-Equity.pdf

BlueGreen Alliance (BGA). (2022, October 13). ***How new investments will deliver good jobs, climate action, and health benefits.*** www.bluegreenalliance.org/site/a-user-guide-to-the-inflation-reduction-act

Bureau of Economic Analysis. (2022, February 8). ***United States census bureau. 2021 Trade gap is $859.1 billion.*** www.bea.gov/sites/default/files/2022-02/trad1221annual-fax.pdf

Córdova, T., Wilson, M. & Stettner, A. (2018, June 6). ***Revitalizing manufacturing and expanding opportunities for Chicago's black and Latino communities.*** The Century Foundation. tcf.org/content/report/revitalizing-manufacturing-expanding-opportunities-chicagos-black-latino-communities

FRED Economic Data: St. Louis Fed. (2023). ***All employees, manufacturing [MANEMP].*** fred.stlouisfed.org/series/MANEMP#

Henderson, T. (2022, September 21). ***The US has reversed pandemic job losses. Most individual states haven't.*** The Pew Charitable Trusts. www.pewtrusts.org/en/research-and-analysis/blogs/stateline/2022/09/21/the-us-has-reversed-pandemic-job-losses-most-individual-states-havent

Hirsch, B.T., Macpherson, D.A., & Even, W.E. (2023, March 22). ***Union membership, coverage, and earnings from the CPS.*** www.unionstats.com

Mishel, L. (2018, March 12). ***Yes, manufacturing still provides a pay advantage, but staffing firm outsourcing is eroding it.*** Economic Policy Institute. www.epi.org/publication/manufacturing-still-provides-a-pay-advantage-but-outsourcing-is-eroding-it

Schencker, L. (2019, June 6). ***Chicago's lifespan gap: Streeterville residents live to 90. Englewood residents die at 60. Study finds it's the largest divide in the U.S. Chicago Tribune.*** www.chicagotribune.com/business/ct-biz-chicago-has-largest-life-expectancy-gap-between-neighborhoods-20190605-story.html

Scott, R.E. (2015, January 22). ***The manufacturing footprint and the importance of U.S. manufacturing jobs.*** Economic Policy Institute. www.epi.org/publication/the-manufacturing-footprint-and-the-importance-of-u-s-manufacturing-jobs

Scott, R.E., Wilson, V., Kandra, J., & Perez, D. (2022, January 31). ***Botched policy responses to globalization have decimated manufacturing employment with often overlooked costs for Black, Brown, and other workers of color.*** Economic Policy Institute. www.epi.org/publication/botched-policy-responses-to-globalization

Swinney, D. (n.d.). ***Hiding in plain sight: How manufacturing can save Chicago.*** Manufacturing Renaissance. mfgren.org/hiding-in-plain-sight-how-manufacturing-can-save-chicago

Telford, T. (2019, September 26). ***Income inequality in America is the highest it's been since Census Bureau started tracking it, data shows.*** www.washingtonpost.com/business/2019/09/26/income-inequality-america-highest-its-been-since-census-started-tracking-it-data-show

Thompson, D. (2017, August 9). ***Restaurants are the new factories.*** www.theatlantic.com/business/archive/2017/08/restaurant-jobs boom/536244

U.S. Department of Labor – Apprenticeship USA. (n.d.). ***What is RAPIDS?*** www.apprenticeship.gov/help/what-rapids

BLUEGREEN ALLIANCE

The BlueGreen Alliance unites labor unions and environmental organizations to solve today's environmental challenges in ways that create and maintain quality jobs and build a clean, thriving, and equitable economy.

Jeff Hurley is the State Initiatives Manager at BlueGreen Alliance and is based in Chicago, IL. Jeff leads policy development and implementation for the Building Clean program and advances state-level policy opportunities in targeted states.

Prior to joining BGA, Jeff worked at the National Conference of State Legislatures, where as a Director of State-Federal Affairs he managed NCSL's legislative agenda and coordinated the association's state-local fiscal relations.

Jeff received his BA from Indiana University and obtained a master's degree in Political Management from the George Washington University.

Embodied Injustices: The Harms Found in Building Material Life Cycles

Veena Singla

&

Rebecca Stamm

Have you ever thought about where the materials in buildings come from, who makes them, and how the chemicals used in manufacturing impact these workers and people who live nearby? What about when a building is rehabilitated or torn down and demolition materials are disposed of — where do the materials go, and who is impacted by this disposal?

When specifying materials, it is critical to consider their entire life cycle, including how manufacturing operations may impact the health of people who live nearby.
Photo: nielubieklonu/iStock

There were few concrete answers to these questions when we started this work in 2020, aiming to inform better material choices by illuminating the life cycle chemical and environmental justice impacts of building materials. We did know that the lived experience of communities near manufacturing facilities spoke about volumes of harm. We wanted to find a way to tell these stories with publicly available data, and to quantify what has been invisible and ignored: the toxic pollution emitted from building material facilities that threatens the health of people in these communities.

BACKGROUND

For decades, the sustainable building sector has focused mostly on considerations that bring financial benefits to building owners and developers. Thus, the major factors driving building material choices have been energy performance and cost. More recently, the life cycle of building materials that contribute to greenhouse gas emissions (embodied carbon) and climate change have also become an important and needed focus. Often overlooked but equally important are the human and environmental health impacts of hazardous chemicals in a product's life cycle (Figure 1).

Hazardous chemicals can negatively impact people and the natural environment in communities near manufacturing and disposal sites. Workers who make, install, or dispose of materials, building occupants, and elements of the natural environment are especially at risk. Hazardous chemicals can also contribute to environmental injustices.

Environmental injustice or environmental racism refers to the fact that pollution and its resultant harmful health impacts fall disproportionately on communities whose members are Black, Indigenous, and/or people of color (BIPOC). Decades of systemic racism and racist policies such as redlining have resulted in a greater concentration of pollution sources, polluting industries, and contaminated sites in BIPOC communities. These same populations, moreover, do not generally reap the benefits from policies and investments that improve community health, such as green infrastructure upgrades or programs to strengthen climate resilience. And often, the

Figure 1. Simplified building materials life cycle and potential impacts of hazardous chemicals at each stage

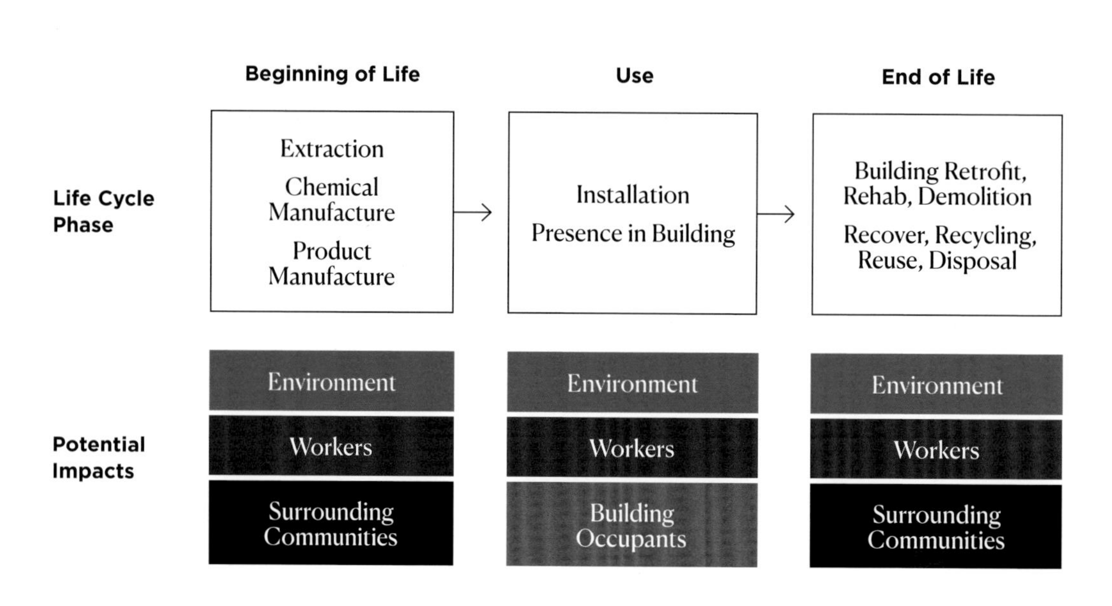

communities located near chemical plants, manufacturing facilities, and disposal sites, including those related to building materials, are disproportionately composed of BIPOC, low-income, and other populations who have been and continue to be excluded from power, processes, and decisions that affect them. The environmental justice movement has worked for decades to reduce environmental, health, economic, and racial disparities for impacted communities. Construction industry professionals have an opportunity, and a responsibility, to support these communities, and they can start by choosing materials that are safer throughout their life cycle.

The environmental justice movement has worked for decades to reduce environmental, health, economic, and racial disparities for impacted communities. Construction industry professionals have an opportunity, and a responsibility, to support these communities, and they can start by choosing materials that are safer throughout their life cycle.

To expand understanding of products' life cycle health and environmental justice impacts, we started with the principles of green chemistry and environmental justice and developed a framework that includes the six major criteria, as outlined in Figure 2.

Using this framework, we examined two widely used insulation materials: fiberglass and spray polyurethane foam (SPF) insulation. We chose insulation because it is a critical element of almost all new construction and many energy efficiency upgrades; it helps provide a comfortable indoor environment and reduces energy use in buildings, but it can also introduce hazardous chemicals. In our prior research focused on use-phase chemical impacts, we identified fiberglass as a preferred insulation material and spray foam as having significant chemical concerns. We chose these materials for additional research because one is among the best in class and one is worst in class, from a chemical hazard perspective.

Using publicly available data and tools such as the Toxics Release Inventory and EJScreen from the United States Environmental Protection Agency, we investigated the manufacture and disposal in the United States of the primary component of spray foam insulation (isocyanates) and the primary component of fiberglass insulation (glass fibers). In general across the criteria, we found that fiberglass is preferable to spray foam, though both materials had negative pollution impacts on BIPOC and/ or low-income communities.

We used the framework to compare the two materials and identify opportunities for life cycle improvements. The following paragraphs share some of our findings.

MATERIALS COMPARISON

Prevent pollution and waste

We analyzed data from the U.S. Environmental Protection Agency (EPA) on waste and releases from isocyanate and glass fiber facilities. Results for the two materials are not directly comparable because there was not enough publicly available information to calculate the amount of waste or releases for a given output of insulation. However, greater total amounts of hazardous releases, regardless of production volume of insulation, can still translate to greater overall impacts on surrounding communities and the environment.

Manufacturing of isocyanates released a much larger amount of hazardous chemicals to the air and water and generated far more overall waste than did glass fiber manufacturing (Figure 3). While the amount of waste was comparatively smaller, the manufacturing of glass fibers still released compounds of major concern such as lead, a toxic metal for which there is no safe level of exposure for children.

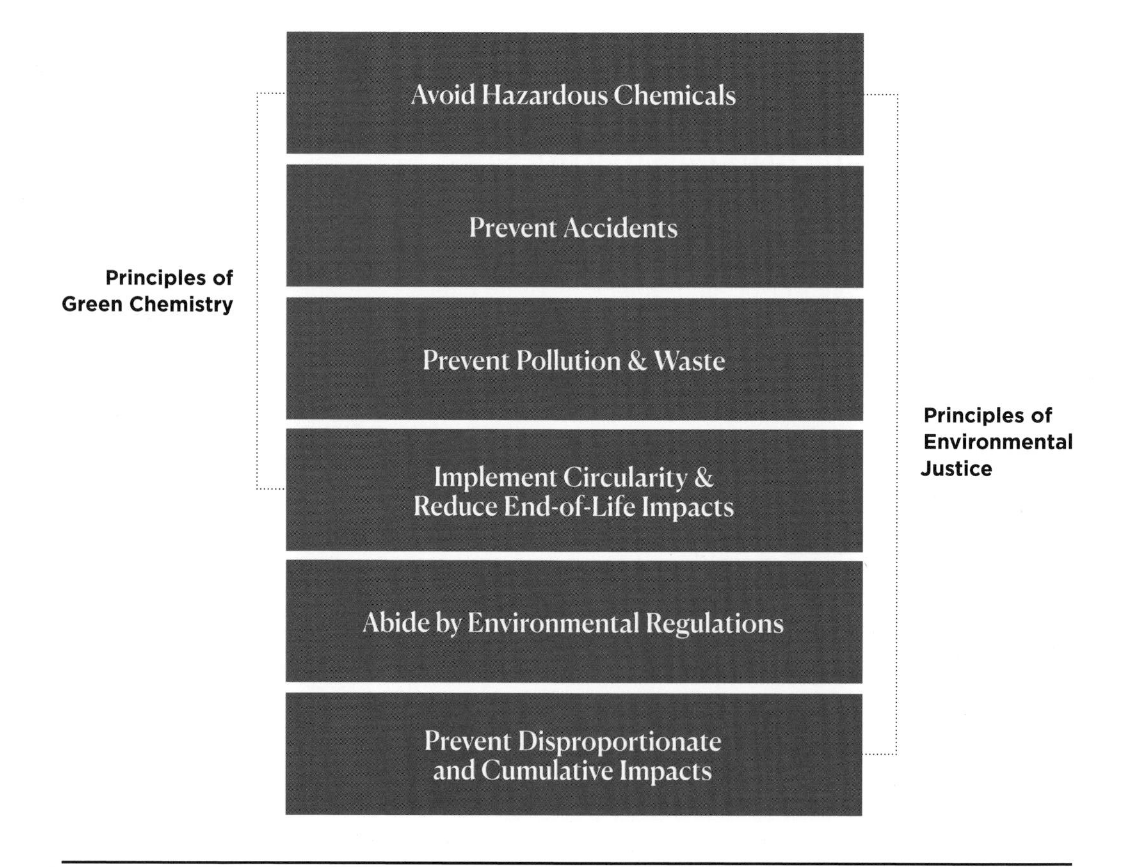

Figure 2. Case study criteria for assessing health and environmental justice impacts based on selected green chemistry and environmental justice principles

Figure 3. Average annual hazardous isocyanate — or glass fiber-related chemicals released to air and water or disposed of as waste for the facilities studied, 2015-2019

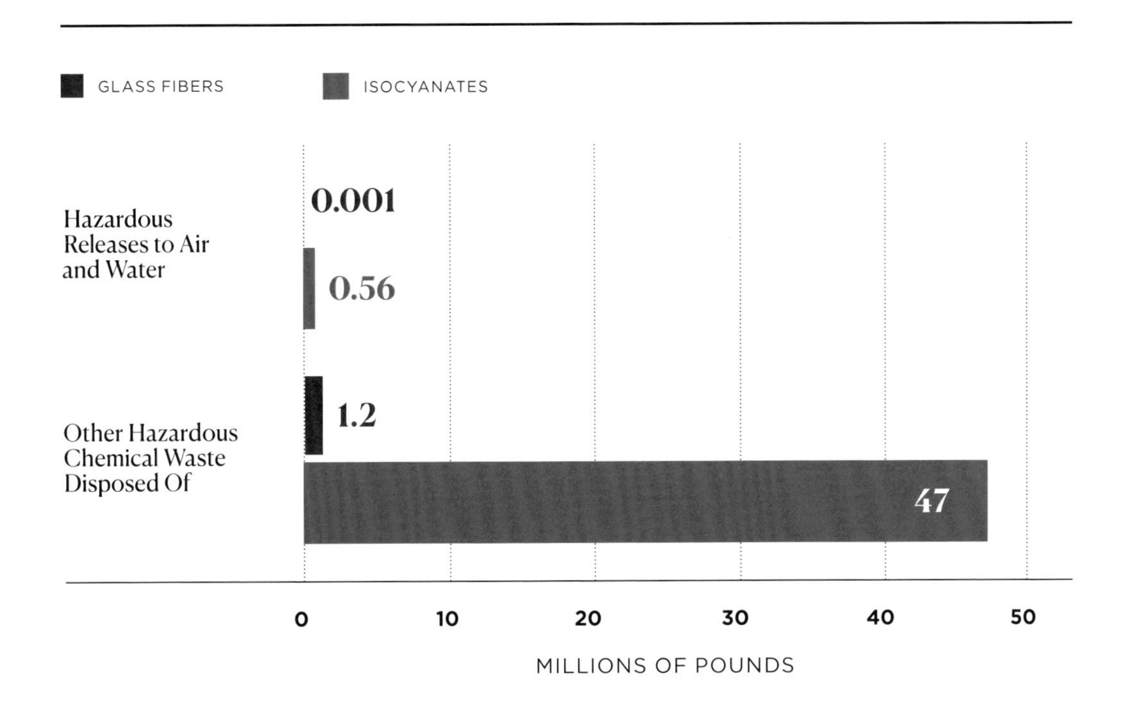

Prevent disproportionate impacts

As discussed earlier, communities of color and low-income communities are disproportionately affected by environmental pollutants. We analyzed facility locations and community demographics to identify localized environmental justice impacts and found that both isocyanate and glass fiber production can contribute to such disproportionate impacts. Isocyanate manufacturing uses and releases hazardous chemicals, as noted above. All four isocyanate facilities in the United States are sited in places that are disproportionately Black, Latino, and/or American Indian/Alaska Native. As for glass fiber manufacturing facilities, the majority are located in or near communities with a percentage of people of color and/or low-income residents that is greater than in the United States overall.

Prevent cumulative impacts

Those facing environmental injustice often suffer from multiple sources of pollution in addition to other stressors, such as poverty and racial discrimination. United States policies have largely failed to evaluate, mitigate, or prevent these cumulative impacts resulting from a combination of stressors over time.

We reviewed EPA data on additional hazardous chemical releases from the glass fiber and isocyanate facilities (from other processes) and on all hazardous chemical

Photo: Art Wager/iStock

releases reportable to the EPA in the cities where those facilities are located.

The four isocyanate manufacturing facilities are located in three cities: two in Geismar, Louisiana, and one each in Baytown, Texas, and Freeport, Texas. Figure 4 illustrates how the releases from these facilities contribute to cumulative hazardous chemical releases in the surrounding communities. Compared with glass fiber manufacturing, the isocyanate facilities are located in cities with much greater total hazardous releases, but both contribute to cumulative impacts.

Geismar has many other industrial facilities besides the two isocyanate manufacturing plants. Combined, these facilities reported releasing more than 15 million pounds of hazardous chemicals in 2019 alone (Figure 4), and EPA data for the past 10 years show an upward trend in the quantity of hazardous releases reported in Geismar.

Geismar is part of the area along the Mississippi River between New Orleans and Baton Rouge known as "Death Alley" (or "Cancer Alley") because of the concentration of industrial activity and associated elevated health risks and deaths. The proportion of Black residents in the community around its isocyanate facilities is more than 2.5 times the proportion of Black residents in the United States overall.

OPPORTUNITIES FOR IMPROVEMENTS

We also used our framework's criteria to identify where manufacturers could make life cycle improvements. For example, fiberglass manufacturers could reduce harmful metal emissions by investing in best available filtration systems in their facilities, as recommended in the European Union. Additionally, selection of glass inputs with low metal content could also reduce metal emissions. There are currently no standard requirements for metal content of glass cullet (the recycled glass input used in fiberglass manufacturing). Industry-wide requirements for low metal content glass cullet could improve the quality of recycled glass used in fiberglass insulation and reduce hazardous metal releases.

The manufacturing of isocyanates uses many hazardous chemicals and does not present much opportunity to improve the hazard profile of chemicals used in the process. The biggest opportunity is to move to different, nonhazardous chemistries or materials.

Figure 4. Isocyanate-related releases to air and water, all releases from isocyanate facilities to air and water, and all releases in the cities where isocyanates are produced

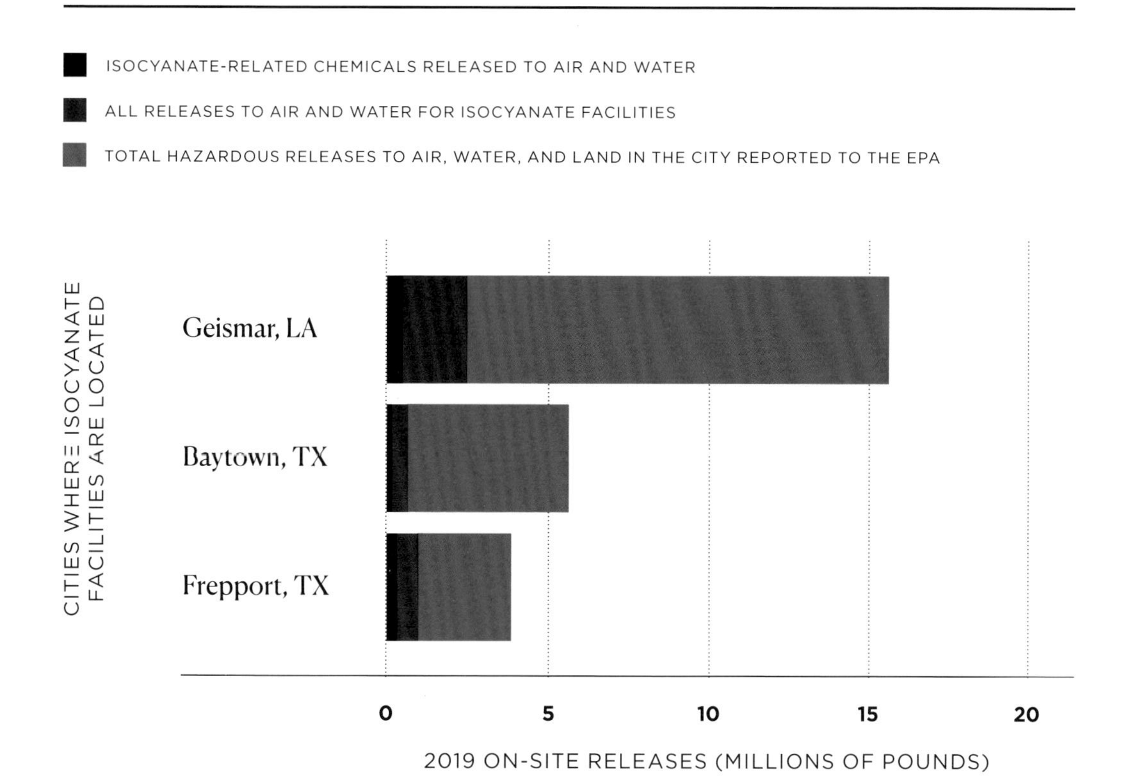

Photo: Charles Deluvio/Unsplash

CONCLUSION

Based on our analysis, we advise choosing fiberglass or other insulation materials with fewer hazardous chemicals than spray foam to reduce life cycle chemical and environmental justice impacts. For more information, see the product guidance on Healthy Building Network's website.[1] Avoiding hazardous chemicals in a product's content is an excellent starting point to help protect not only building occupants and installers, but also others impacted by those hazardous chemicals throughout the supply chain.

Our analysis found significant chemical and environmental justice impacts over the life cycle of two important building materials. To truly create an equitable and sustainable built environment, we must not perpetuate these impacts. Climate solutions, such as building insulation, should advance the well-being of all communities, not just those that are privileged in society.

We recommend that embodied chemical and environmental justice impacts be key considerations in decision making for all building materials. The framework we have developed can be applied to any other chemical or material to identify opportunities to reduce impacts or to compare materials. By choosing materials with fewer embodied impacts, and advocating to improve building material life cycles, we can start to transform our materials system from one that harms communities to one that supports healthy environments and healthy families.

1 healthybuilding.net/reports

Veena Singla is a Senior Scientist with the Natural Resources Defense Council and Adjunct Assistant professor at Columbia University. Her work seeks to address health disparities linked to harmful environmental exposures using an interdisciplinary approach incorporating environmental health, exposure science, public health and policy expertise. Her research investigates how toxic chemicals and pollution related to systems of materials use, production and disposal threaten the health of impacted communities.

She currently serves on the US EPA's Children's Health Protection Advisory Committee, the National Toxicology Program Board of Scientific Counselors, the Board of Directors for Clean Production Action, and as Associate Director for the Agents of Change in Environmental Justice Program. She completed a postdoctoral teaching fellowship at Stanford University and was an adjunct faculty member at the University of San Francisco. She holds a bachelor's degree from the University of California, Berkeley, and a PhD in cell biology from UCSF.

Rebecca Stamm is passionate about improving human and environmental health through safer products. As Senior Researcher at Healthy Building Network, she works with the team to conduct vital research on the life cycle chemical impacts of materials to drive transparency and innovation. She currently serves on the Health Product Declaration Collaborative (HPDC) Technical Committee and is co-chair of the HPDC Social Equity Technical Sub-Group. Rebecca has a B.S. from Rose-Hulman Institute of Technology and a M.S. from Purdue University, where she studied Chemical Engineering, and has worked extensively in building product and chemical hazard research.

NATURAL RESOURCES DEFENSE COUNCIL

NRDC (Natural Resources Defense Council) is an international nonprofit environmental organization with more than 3 million members and online activists. Since 1970, our lawyers, scientists, and other environmental specialists have worked to protect the world's natural resources, public health, and the environment. NRDC has offices in New York City, Washington, D.C., Los Angeles, San Francisco, Chicago, Bozeman, and Beijing.

HEALTHY BUILDING NETWORK

Since 2000, Healthy Building Network (HBN) has defined the leading edge of healthy building practices that increase transparency in the building products industry, reduce human exposure to hazardous chemicals, and create market incentives for healthier innovations in manufacturing. We are a team of researchers, engineers, scientists, building experts, and educators, and we pursue our mission on three fronts:

1. **Research and policy** — uncovering cutting-edge information about healthier products and health impacts;
2. **Data tools** — producing innovative software platforms that ensure product transparency and catalog chemical hazards; and
3. **Education and capacity building** — fostering others' capabilities to make informed decisions.

As a nonprofit organization, we do work that broadly benefits the public, especially children and the most marginalized communities, who suffer disproportionate health impacts from exposure to toxic chemicals. We work to reduce toxic chemical use, minimize hazards, and eliminate exposure for all.

Addressing Injustice through Healthy Affordable Housing

Susan Puri

I was recently introduced to Drayton Jackson, the Executive Director of the Foundation for Homeless and Poverty Management, a non-profit organization in Kitsap County, Washington, focused on breaking patterns of generational poverty. Drayton's foundation is leading an initiative to develop a new affordable housing complex that will provide housing units along with multiple services such as a daycare and a 24-hour library — the first of its kind in Washington State. His mission of working to alleviate poverty and homelessness came from his more than two decades of personally living through homelessness. He explained that, as a youth, he also suffered from the adverse effects of lead poisoning due to peeling paint in his housing project in Brooklyn, as well as asthma from the industrial pollution in the air. In addition, he said that these types of health impacts were rampant among his peers and playmates living in the housing project, as were roach infestations. To his

Atmospheric pollution and toxic chemicals such as lead in the buildings themselves cause lasting harm, especially in children. Photo: Avi Werde/Unsplash

knowledge, no one told his mother about the risk of lead poisoning from peeling paint and how that might affect her children's health and development.

The health of residents is a top priority in Drayton's new affordable housing project. The lead architect is Gladys Ly-Au Young of SKL Architects, an active member of ILFI's Affordable Housing Program who has been working diligently for years to help transform the healthy materials options available for affordable housing. When Gladys told him about the need to build affordable housing with products that do not detrimentally impact the health of the people living there, he reflected on his own life experiences and told us that he had found his "why" for taking up this issue as well.

At the end of 2021, I was researching the closure of the West Calumet Housing Complex in East Chicago, Indiana, in order to write an article on ILFI's blog "Trim Tab" about the completion of a new housing development in that community called Harbor Square. This project is striving for ILFI's Zero Energy Certification and participating in our Affordable Housing Program. I knew the basic story of the closure from the project team's initial application to ILFI as a pilot project: the complex had been forced to close due to lead and arsenic contamination in the soil, and it was now an EPA Superfund site. One thousand residents had lived there at the time, including 700 children, many of whom continue to suffer health impacts from this exposure. The new project (one of several being built in the area) would include 28 housing units and a community medical facility and would more than likely include many former residents of the West Calumet complex, who were now all displaced from their homes and struggling to find housing.

No one told them that their housing complex was built on top of a former lead smelting plant (USS Steel), and now no one was telling them where to go or giving them assistance for their health issues. Although there was folklore in the neighborhood that they lived on ground contaminated with lead, no one knew for sure. What the community members did know was that their children were suffering — many of them had development delays and physical health impacts.

In my five years working with affordable housing pilot projects at ILFI, this was, unfortunately, far from the first time that I had been told about environmental injustices and hazardous exposures like this in low-income communities, particularly in communities of color. However, this was the first time that I had heard of a housing complex being turned into an EPA Superfund site, even though public housing complexes situated very near EPA Superfund sites are, sadly, far from rare. The article I was writing was intended to be celebratory — all of us at ILFI were thrilled to hear of the grand opening of the Harbor Square project and their initial success in creating a Zero Energy multi-family structure — but I also wanted to provide more background information on the project's context and the difficult issues facing the residents in that area. I found an article on EarthJustice written by Akeeshea Daniels, a mother who had lived with her sons in the West Calumet Housing Complex for 12 years. She expressed the same sentiment that Drayton felt about his childhood exposure to toxic chemicals in his environment — no one told us. No one told them that their housing complex was built on top of a former lead smelting plant (USS Steel), and now no one was telling them where to go or giving them assistance for their health issues. Although there was

Photo: Darren Townsend/iStock

folklore in the neighborhood that they lived on ground contaminated with lead, no one knew for sure. What the community members did know was that their children were suffering — many of them had development delays and physical health impacts. Akeeshea noticed learning delays in her younger son when he was two years old and struggling in preschool, something she had not seen in her older children. Her son now has multiple permanent health issues, including ADHD, asthma, and allergies. "Experts say the first five years of a child's life are the most important for their development," Akeeshea wrote. "Experts also say no amount of lead is safe. Now I know my kids and my neighbors didn't have a chance. The water, the air, the soil and dust in West Calumet poisoned their developing brains. And now, we are living with irreversible damage."

Reading Akeeshea's story, I felt rage boil inside me as I thought of my own two-year old son and all the mental energy that I expend every day trying to keep him safe. I wondered just how devastated I would be if this had happened to my child. However, through no fault of their own, this type of environmental injustice — really, environmental racism — is a reality for parents and family members throughout the country. Many of us have sat through (and probably given) presentations with maps showing "Cancer Alley" and correlations between diseases, incomes, race, and the history of redlined neighborhoods. I could cite many depressing statistics showing the disproportionate health burden of mold, mildew, pest infestations, and poor air quality borne by low-income and BIPOC communities, not to mention the drastically unequal utility burdens that put people at great risk during extreme weather events. The outcomes of these inequalities produce even more depressing statistics around the prevalence of asthma, autoimmune conditions, and various cancers. When we talk about lifespans being predictable based on your income, your zip code, and even your race, this is what we are talking about. Yes, inequitable access to medical care is a component, as are other social welfare issues. However, those of us working to create buildings must remember that "neighborhood and built environment" is one of the five social determinants of health, which are considered by the CDC to account for 80 to 90 percent of modifiable contributing factors to health outcomes.

If you were to search on the internet for "environmental justice maps," you would find the EPA's EJScreen and dozens of other mapping tools. All this information is critical to defining the problem. However, we need to move beyond citing statistics — and we definitely need to move beyond thinking these types of discriminatory policies and disproportionate burdens are in our past. Now is the time for action. Just as this decade has been called "the one that matters" for climate change, we must concurrently address the interlinked problems of homelessness and toxic exposures. While we are still cleaning up disastrous exposures like the one at the West Calumet Housing Complex and the more quotidian exposures of peeling lead paint that Drayton faced (and that an estimated 1.1 million other low-income households continue to face), we need to ensure we do not repeat the cycle by creating additional problems for future generations to clean up.

There is no reason why affordable housing should be built or renovated with materials that are less healthy than those that we

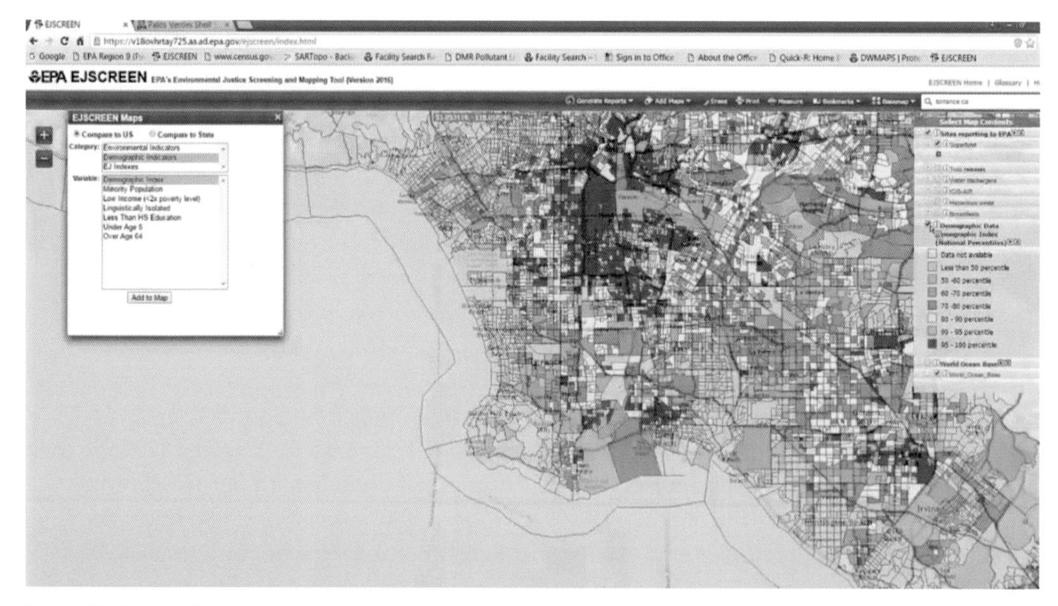

By considering a number of environmental and socioeconomic metrics, the EPA's EJScreen can help design professionals better understand the vulnerabilities of a particular community. Credit: US EPA www.epa.gov/ejscreen.

install in high-end office space or market-rate housing, unless we are willing to say that we believe people with fewer resources deserve to be less healthy. There is a very logical argument that, given all the discriminatory policies of the past and the impacts these have had on the health outcomes of entire communities, we should be prioritizing affordable housing in our goal of Red List Free buildings. Building multi-family or single-family affordable housing today likely affects many people uniquely vulnerable to health impacts of poor air quality, toxic chemicals, or other environmental hazards, due to the current inequalities in health that are prevalent in our communities.

This is why ILFI has chosen to prioritize affordable housing within our work. We believe a Living Future is a just future, and that vision includes everyone. ILFI has worked with dozens of affordable housing project teams since the first project of this kind registered in 2011. Using Red List Free materials is increasingly becoming easier for all project teams, thanks to accelerating momentum within the transparency movement and a growing knowledge of and push towards using healthier products in buildings for the benefit of all. This includes anyone who may be exposed to the material, from production to occupancy to eventual deconstruction and demolition. ILFI is committed to ensuring that these advances in materials don't just "trickle down" to those living in affordable housing, but that we place affordable housing at the forefront of our goals for a healthier and regenerative Living Future.

Susan Puri is the Director of Affordable Housing and has been with ILFI for four and a half years. She oversees the creation of resources, education, events, and other programmatic support for the Institute's Affordable Housing Program.

Originally from the Atlanta area, Susan attended Georgia Tech where she received a Bachelor of Architecture and a Masters of City and Regional Planning, with a focus on Affordable Housing Development. Prior to joining ILFI, Susan worked in architecture, green building consulting, and urban planning. After five years in the Pacific Northwest, she has recently relocated back to Atlanta.

Photo: Lindsay Henwood/Unsplash

PART II:

Health

Stay Out of the Red Zone

WHAT'S IN THERE MATTERS

Dana Bourland

By the time I was seventeen years old, I had moved eleven times. Because of my own experience moving from place to place, I have spent the better part of the last several decades focused on making sure everyone has a place to call home — that everyone enjoys the human right to housing.

But it was not until my time at Enterprise Community Partners, a nonprofit focused on community development and affordable housing, that I understood just how much the methods and materials we employ to realize that human right matter. The building materials that are used to construct our homes absolutely make a difference to our human and planetary health. And while we can pick up a bag of chips or box of cereal and read the ingredients list to know what ingredients are inside, that is not possible when we rent or purchase a home. Much of my work now focuses on investing in opportunities that eliminate classes of toxic chemicals from use in our housing supply chain. And it's a long supply chain that intersects with schools, offices, hospitals, and places of worship. There are tremendous openings to do better that could simultaneously promote worker health, community health, and planetary

The aptly named "Deckony" at the PAE Living Building in Portland, Oregon, offers the expanse and fresh air of a rooftop deck combined with the indoor/outdoor feel of a balcony. Non-toxic materials and biophilic design create a fifth-floor oasis for occupants. Photo: Lara Swimmer, courtesy of PAE Engineers

health — in one fell swoop, as I like to say — by ending the cycle of pollution inherent within our building supply system.

No one is immune to this pervasive problem of toxic chemical exposure in the built environment. In 2012, I leased an apartment in a building on the Upper West Side of New York City that was certified as a green building by the United States Green Building Council. During that time, I participated in a pilot study with the Environmental Defense Fund. I wore a bracelet that used wristband monitoring technology from MyExposome, Inc., developed at Oregon State University, to detect hidden chemical exposures in my living environment. There were twenty-seven other people in the study, and the technology could detect up to 1,400 chemicals. Much to my horror, my wristband detected eleven chemicals, including persistent, bioaccumulative, and toxic substances. They are as scary as they sound. Bioaccumulative chemicals persist in the environment for generations and build up in the body over time. One of these chemicals was a polycyclic aromatic hydrocarbon, which is an air pollutant linked to cancer. Others included phthalates, which are used to make plastics more durable, and flame retardant chemicals, often used in upholstery, clothing, and common cooking utensils, pots, and pans. I was not the exception: every participant's

Photo: gahsoon/iStock

wristband detected harmful chemicals. And while I write about this in my book, *Gray to Green Communities*, it was on a recent tour of work in North Minneapolis where this toxic reality hit home again.

While on this wonderful tour, which led us around public assets that the community was reimagining, I walked several blocks from a large park to the Mississippi River to enjoy a new overlook area. The initially pleasant walk became less so as we crossed a highway, where there was no longer a connected sidewalk. We began walking next to large trucks. Soon, my throat became dry and my eyes started itching, and I noticed a chemical taste in my mouth. When I finally looked around to understand why this was happening, I realized I was standing directly in front of a cement factory. The cement making process involves crushing and grinding the limestone and then heating the limestone with other materials to create "clinker." The clinker is then mixed with gypsum to eventually create cement. We were inhaling the emissions from these processes and in this case, since the limestone was hauled in from other sites, we were also breathing in the exhaust from the trucks.

When we produce ingredients for materials that are harmful, the pollution is not contained in the building product but envelops the communities where it is produced. Many other people and natural spaces are exposed when the product is transported to the next facility. I remember, embarrassingly now, that I once thought it was elegant to take waste fly ash generated from the process of burning coal and store it in concrete. Coal ash contains mercury, cadmium, and arsenic, and it is often stored in unlined ponds, where these toxins can leak into groundwater. Utilizing it in concrete provides an alternative place to store toxic waste, and you do not need to use as much cement in the concrete. Yet everything about this scenario is wrong. It incentivizes the production of coal ash, and it continues to create opportunities for human exposure to known toxicants. There's nothing green, safe, or healthy about incorporating hazardous byproducts within building materials.

There is a buzz among environmental philanthropists right now around "decarbonization." This talk amounts mostly to an interest in removing oil and gas-burning HVAC systems, water heaters, and stoves. While of course this step is necessary, we cannot truly decarbonize buildings, including our homes, until we take a comprehensive approach that explores the many ways that pollutants, namely greenhouse gases and plastics made from fossil fuels, move into all aspects of the built environment. This survey must include everything from flooring and other surfaces to pervasively used materials like polyvinyl chloride (PVC) and concrete.

There is no dispute that we must increase the supply of safe housing that is affordable to people of all incomes everywhere across the United States. If we do this without considering material health, we will accelerate planetary and human suffering while locking in carbon emissions, making it virtually impossible to thwart catastrophic consequences from climate change. And because toxic classes of chemicals accumulate in buildings, when an extreme weather event destroys whole neighborhoods, it makes it dangerous to clean up and rebuild. As Henry David Thoreau famously wrote, "What is the use of a house, if you haven't got a tolerable

HIGH-IMPACT MATERIALS

Some materials have a greater impact when it comes to their emissions and pollution impacts. According to Architecture 2050, just three materials — concrete, aluminum, and steel — are responsible for 23 percent of global emissions and the associated pollution and health impacts. Thankfully, concrete is getting some attention through the United States government's Buy Clean Initiative, a procurement policy that takes into account the carbon and pollution impacts of materials used in federal projects. The federal government is prioritizing low carbon procurement in four categories: steel, concrete, asphalt, and flat glass, and will use Environmental Product Declarations (EPDs) to compare products.

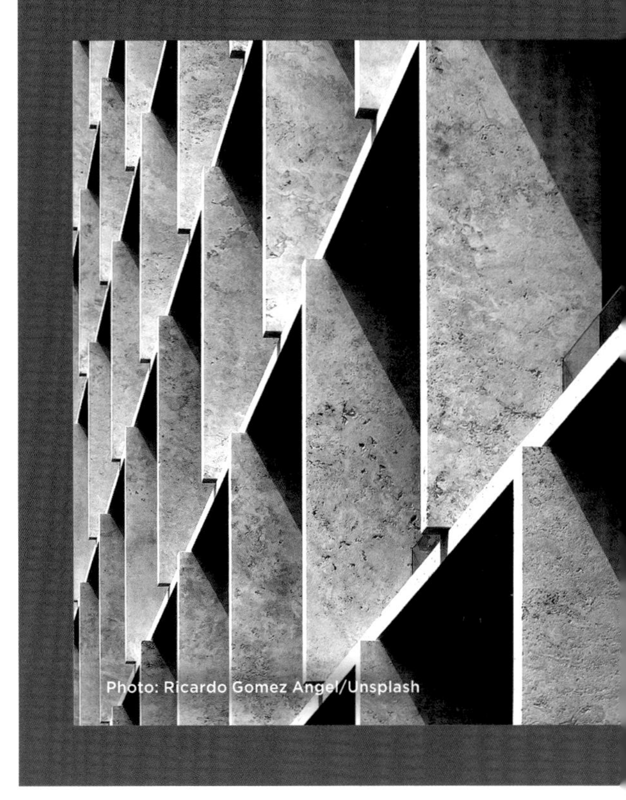
Photo: Ricardo Gomez Angel/Unsplash

planet to put it on?" In addition, what is the use of a house if it creates intolerable conditions for the communities that produce the ingredients and products used in its construction? And, shouldn't homes shelter us from persistent, bioaccumulative, and toxic chemicals?

As we rush to do all we can to avert catastrophic impacts from climate change, and as we simultaneously pay attention to planetary boundaries, we must do better when it comes to the extraction, production, and installation of materials we are specifying, purchasing and using in our homes and buildings.

As we rush to do all we can to avert catastrophic impacts from climate change, and as we simultaneously pay attention to planetary boundaries, we must do better when it comes to the extraction, production, and installation of materials we are specifying, purchasing and using in our homes and buildings. To help stop the cycle of pollution and to avoid making some communities green at the expense of making other ones gray, we must consistently ask the questions: What is in this product? And where do the ingredients come from?

Already today, we have access to the science that provides evidence about the impact of these toxic classes of chemicals on our health. We know that our "gray" housing practices are making us sick and that our reliance on fossil fuels is choking our planet. Fortunately, comprehensive and holistic green housing is achievable and is proven to reduce carbon emissions while boosting health and economic outcomes. We can refer to the work of organizations like the Healthy Building Network to make better choices and avoid the Red List of known carcinogens. In addition to the Healthy Building Network, JPB is supporting other organizations involved in this work, including the Green Science Policy Institute, Blue Green Alliance, Healthy Product Declaration Collaborative, and the Healthy Materials Lab at Parsons. I am most excited by what knowing better means for new jobs, for inventing new products that can be cleanly manufactured in the United States, and for how these choices can help end the cycle of pollution because such products can be cleanly reused, repurposed, or even recycled.

While we do not have bracelets for buildings to make seen what is currently invisible, to steal the tagline of Healthy Building Network, we do know better, so let's do better together. Let's end the bioaccumulation of harmful chemicals in our bodies, our communities, and in our atmosphere. We can use our purchasing power to demand better materials and products, and we can organize our friends and neighbors to demand better. Let us continue innovating to drive down the price and increase the effectiveness of green materials. The health and well-being of everyone and the planet depend on it. Let us act like this is true, if not for us, then for our children and our children's children.

Dana Bourland, AICP is a thought leader advancing solutions that enable a thriving planet and well-being for all. She led the creation of the Environment Program at The JPB Foundation by investing in a just, equitable and clean energy future, increasing access to the benefits of nature, detoxifying the built and natural systems, and building power for environmental justice. Formerly Dana created a successful movement to green all affordable housing in the United States during her tenure as Vice President for Enterprise Community Partners where she led environmental strategy for the national affordable housing and community development intermediary. Dana is the author of *Gray to Green: A Call to Action on the Housing and Climate Crises* published by Island Press. Dana is a graduate of Harvard's Graduate Program in Real Estate and holds a Master of Planning Degree from the Humphrey Institute. She was named one of Fast Company Magazine's Most Influential Women Activists in Technology and is featured in and has contributed to numerous publications and addressed global audiences on issues related to green community development. Dana is a Returned Peace Corps Volunteer, an Ironman finisher, runner, potter, and avid traveler.

THE JPB FOUNDATION

JPB's mission is to advance opportunity in the United States through transformational initiatives that empower those living in poverty, enrich and sustain our environment, and enable pioneering medical research. JPB's Environment Program enables resilient communities by listening, learning, and partnering with people in ways that are accountable to and benefit low-income communities and disinvested communities of color. The Environment Program supports organizations and projects advancing a just and equitable clean energy future, protecting the right of all people to live, work, and play in places that are free from pollution and toxic chemicals, restoring and significantly increasing the presence of parks, green playgrounds, trees, connected trails, and natural areas nationwide, and supporting environmental justice communities.

While at Enterprise Community Partners advancing green affordable housing, I was aware of the Living Building Challenge and I knew that the Materials Petal was a major barrier, particularly for those projects on fixed development budgets. In 2014, during my early years at JPB I recommended, and the Board approved a $1.5M grant to Aeon, a community development corporation in Minnesota, so it could pursue the Materials Petal at The Rose.

Healthy Materials as a Foundation for More Circular Workplaces

Robin Bass

&

Lauren Sparandara

Since our founding, Google has been deeply committed to environmental sustainability. In 2007, we became the first major company to achieve carbon-neutral operations (Pichai, 2020). Over the past decade, Google purchased more renewable energy than any other company, and we became the first major company to match 100 percent of our annual electricity use with renewable energy in 2017 (Google, 2022). We've set a goal to achieve net-zero emissions across our operations and value chain, including our consumer hardware products, by 2030 (Brandt, 2022).

A key part of our plan to reach net-zero is becoming a more circular Google. The Ellen MacArthur Foundation estimates (n.d.) that transitioning to a circular economy by 2050 can save 10 billion tonnes of greenhouse gas emissions a year — one-fifth of the global annual total. The path to zero carbon includes maximizing our reuse of finite resources and prioritizing regenerative, healthy materials.

Charleston East expands the boundaries of sustainable design with flexible workspaces, healthy and reclaimed materials, and public spaces the whole community can enjoy.

We strive for regenerative design in our workplaces by envisioning a built environment where our buildings positively impact our local environments. A major component of this approach is prioritizing circular materials from the outset of design. By starting with healthy materials we're supporting eventual reuse, because a healthy, non-toxic material today can safely become a circular material in the future.

As part of Google's real estate and workplace services team, we strive to incorporate circularity into the design, construction, and operation of our offices in nearly 60 countries around the world. Our holistic approach includes (though isn't limited to) integrating healthy materials into our spaces, establishing responsible procurement standards, and pursuing deconstruction and reuse wherever possible.

Our focus on specifying healthy materials all started when we borrowed a good habit of our engineering teams: asking a lot of questions.

QUESTIONING THAT "NEW SPACE SMELL"

One of Google's core philosophies is to focus on the user. That's certainly true of our product design for consumers. It's also true of the way we approach sustainable buildings and offices for our workers. For more than a decade, our real estate and workplace services teams have focused on how our workspaces impact the health, well-being, and productivity of our employees.

Whenever we opened new facilities, we'd pose questions about the "new space smell" coming from the carpeting and paint (Google, 2019).

What chemicals are producing that odor?

What about the toxins we can't smell?

What are we really breathing in our offices?

How is it affecting our health?

Early on, we found these questions hard to answer. We realized that comprehensive health standards for chemicals and materials in building products didn't really exist. So in 2010 we launched an effort to prioritize

Charleston East is on track to attain the International Living Future Institute (ILFI) Living Building Challenge (LBC) Materials Petal Certification. Using the LBC Red List as a framework, thousands of materials on the project went through a rigorous sourcing and review process.

healthy materials — products that we know contain safer, less hazardous chemicals — in our workspaces.

Dovetailing with Google's mission to organize the world's information and make it universally accessible and useful, our healthy materials program aimed to shed light on the composition of common building materials. We began working closely with manufacturers to understand the safety and transparency of their building products, to find ways of making this information more widely available, and to leverage third-party standards that help compare materials health across products.

Our goal was to adopt healthier materials for our workplace — and to encourage stronger standards for the building industry at large. Because it takes more than one company to make an impact on the circular economy. As we've said before (Google, 2019), it takes thousands of companies joining us in this effort for healthy materials to make their way onto consumer shelves and into typical building designs.

INTEGRATING HEALTHY MATERIALS INTO OUR SPACES

Today, integrating healthy, circular materials into our spaces is a core part of our sustainable building strategy. We specify healthy materials in the design phase, procure them during construction, and follow best-in-class practices for ventilation and filtration to ensure good indoor air quality. We're constantly seeking new promising technologies and breakthrough approaches to material design, the elimination of waste, and the reuse of resources.

A leading example of this integrated approach was our work on the Charleston East campus in Mountain View, California. Early in the design process, we targeted Living Building Challenge (LBC) Materials Petal certification, which requires that the selection of building materials be consistent with a non-toxic, transparent, and socially equitable approach. In pursuit of this goal, and to encourage industry transparency, we worked with manufacturers to vet every one of the 6,800-plus building products (Google, *Healthy Workplaces*) used at Charleston East against the "Red List" of ingredients, which catalogs 816 worst-in-class chemicals (Sparandara, n.d.). This is the first time that we've attempted such an effort at this scale at Google, with hopes of pushing the building and construction industry toward a focus on material health and transparency.

We continued to prioritize healthy materials during the construction of Charleston East. The Forest Stewardship Council (FSC) certified 100 percent of the timber used in the construction (2022), including temporary wood used for things like concrete formwork. Although temporary construction materials aren't always a focus of sustainability standards, we went the extra mile by responsibly sourcing all lumber for the project to minimize the footprint of the campus's complex construction.

Charleston East also aimed to divert more than 90 percent of its construction waste from landfills (Google, *Circular Solutions*). All workers on site received training on

A bird's-eye view of the second floor workspace at Google's Bay View development project shows how thousands of Googlers can be in a connected space with individual team neighborhoods under an inspiring canopy. All carpet procured for the building meets strict health criteria. Photo: Iwan Baan

zero-waste practices, and dedicated staff categorized waste materials by type. We implemented a closed-loop system that enabled us to recycle over 530,000 pounds of drywall waste. Whenever possible, we used prefabricated materials to reduce scrap, and worked closely with suppliers to cut down on packaging.

We extended our use of circular materials to the interior construction as well. Charleston East incorporates 30 different types of salvaged materials, such as bike racks, lockers, and tiles.

Our focus on healthy, circular materials at Charleston East pushed us to expand our view of building materials, considering not only their impacts on people in our workplaces but also the impact of these materials on the building's supply chain, from construction to end of life. We're taking these lessons learned from Charleston East and incorporating them elsewhere in our portfolio to help ensure healthy materials are specified and retained in the built environment. We learned that two big levers we can deploy today are responsible procurement standards and planning for reuse and deconstruction.

ESTABLISHING RESPONSIBLE PROCUREMENT STANDARDS

Much of the work to ensure a circular building starts before design, construction, or operation with the creation of strong sustainability standards. Google's real estate team establishes standards for the procurement of healthy, circular materials in a number of areas. One illustrative example is our standards for carpet (Melton, 2023).

Our carpet procurement standards anchor around four areas critical for vetting regenerative materials: third-party certification, circularity criteria, health criteria, and embodied carbon.

Third-Party Validation: Our modular carpet procurement standard leverages industry leading third-party disclosure tools like Cradle to Cradle, Health Product Declaration, and Declare to create consistent chemical disclosure baselines and validate the quality of the data so we can be confident about a manufacturer's product claims.

Circularity: To hit our circularity standards, carpet tiles must be made of at least 45 percent recycled material (and at least 7 percent post-consumer material), installed with a type of adhesive that allows for easy removal and replacement, and backed by a manufacturer take-back agreement. This approach helps promote reuse throughout the carpet's life cycle.

Health: To reach our health standard, carpet procurement should comply with certain indoor air quality requirements, demonstrate a commitment to transparency through a declaration of content from an approved certification list, and must not contain a set of specific harmful materials (including PVCs).

Embodied carbon: Finally, our carpet products must have a global warming potential at least 20 percent lower than the typical baseline from the Carbon Leadership Forum, a leading organization.

We've published these carpet procurement standards so others can adapt them for their own portfolios and adopt elements that might work best for them (Melton, 2023).

A fork lift loads stacks of wood doors, salvaged from a Google interior renovation project, onto the back of a truck to get ready for donation.

PURSUING BUILDING DECONSTRUCTION AND MATERIAL REUSE

Every workspace eventually outlives its original purpose and must adapt to keep up with the needs of a business. Planning ahead for these subsequent phases of a building and office space is critical for circularity and material reuse — and for climate impact. The creation of new buildings and building materials accounts for 11 percent of global carbon emissions (Puettmann, 2021).

Since 2012, the Google real estate team has salvaged more than 1,000 tons of

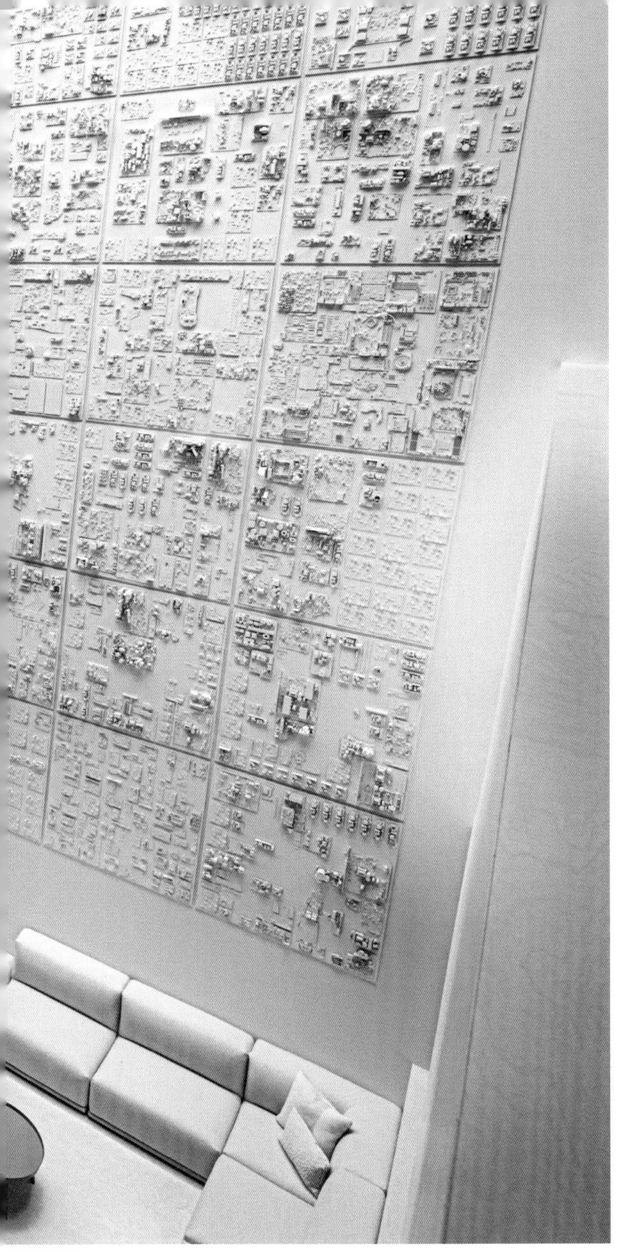

237 MPD, a Google LBC Materials Petal renovation project in Sunnyvale, CA, features salvaged materials throughout the project. Showcased salvaged material installations include the circuit board art wall.

material for reuse. This includes everything from reusing building materials in other office developments to donating furniture to organizations. In 2019, we published a white paper (Sparandara, 2019), along with the Ellen MacArthur Foundation, outlining some of our lessons learned from our deconstruction and reuse work for others in the commercial building industry to consider. One of our biggest insights was that designing with healthy materials in the first place is the foundation for any successful salvage effort. By procuring healthy materials from the outset, we are clearing a path for the next tenant to safely occupy a space or for another organization to extend the life of a piece of furniture.

Data remains a challenge when it comes to building salvage programs — but it's also an opportunity. Exciting new tools and services have emerged that make it possible to assess the components of building materials and to create digital inventories that enable an active salvage market. We continue to explore ways of not only incorporating these tools into our own practices but helping them reach others as well.

Figure 1. Resource Cycles from Commercial Deconstruction (Sparandara, 2019)

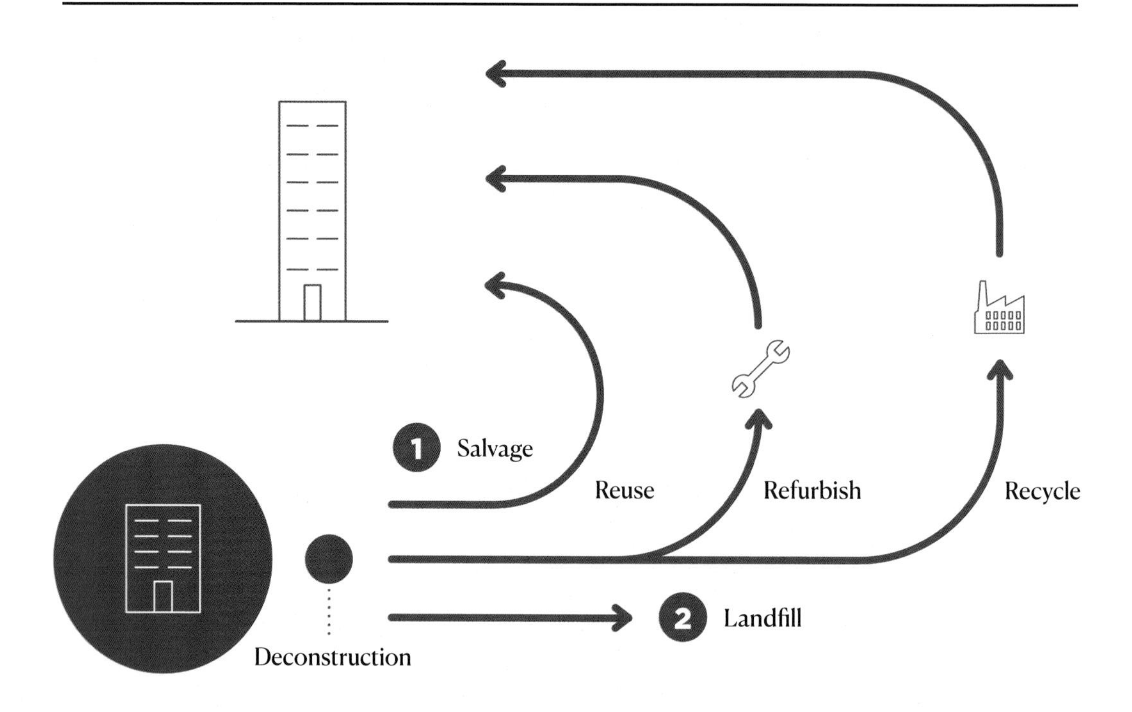

WORKING TOWARD MORE SUSTAINABLE WORKPLACES — TOGETHER

Our efforts to create more circular offices and campuses don't end with healthy materials and building reuse. We're also working to reduce waste across our operations, including building and construction. We have implemented strategies to reduce plastic waste (including single-use plastics), and we're striving to reduce food waste, with a goal of sending zero food waste to landfills — and cutting food waste in half for each Google employee — by 2025 (Bakker, 2022). It's part of a holistic program to design and operate campuses for a future that's low-carbon, zero-waste, nature-rich, and water-positive.

We started this journey by asking questions about how to make our workspaces healthier. We still ask those questions today, but we also ask ourselves how we can share lessons, ideas, and approaches to help others who are tackling similar challenges across the global real estate industry. The beauty of the circular economy is that it connects everyone. That means we need to embrace its challenges together — and also collaborate on new solutions.

Robin Bass leads sustainability programs for the built environment at Google. Her team delivers outcomes for Carbon Free Buildings, Material Circularity, Water Stewardship and Biodiversity in the global campuses and communities that Google calls home. She is a mom, daughter, wife, and sister and enjoys roller skating as a low-carbon mode of transportation and time machine to her 12-year-old self.

Lauren Sparandara is a green building professional with over 15 years of experience championing green building projects in California and across the globe. For the last eight years she has worked at Google, where she is currently a Bay Area Sustainability Partner for the real estate team, advancing efforts to optimize built environments for the health and performance of Googlers and the natural environment. Prior to Google, she was a Senior Green Building Consultant for the DNV GL Group. Lauren obtained her environmental management degree from Yale University and her architecture degree from Washington University in St. Louis. She is a LEED Fellow and a Living Future Hero.

REFERENCES

Bakker, M. (2022, March 7). ***Two new pledges to reduce food loss and waste at Google. Google.*** blog.google/outreach-initiatives/sustainability/two-new-pledges-reduce-food-loss-and-waste-google/

Brandt, K. (2022, November 1). ***Accelerating climate action at Google and beyond.*** Google. blog.google/outreach-initiatives/sustainability/cop27-google-climate-action/

Ellen MacArthur Foundation. (n.d.). ***Building a world free from waste and pollution.*** Retrieved May 12, 2023, from ellenmacarthurfoundation.org/articles/building-a-world-free-from-waste-and-pollution

Forest Stewardship Council. (2022, October 12). ***2022 FSC Leadership Awards Winners Advance Responsible Forest Management.*** us.fsc.org/en-us/newsroom/newsletter/id/1260

Google. (2022, June). ***Google Environmental Report.*** www.gstatic.com/gumdrop/sustainability/google-2022-environmental-report.pdf

Google. (2019, September). ***The journey toward healthier materials.*** sustainability.google/progress/projects/smelling-the-carpet/

Google. (n.d.). ***Circular Resources.*** Retrieved May 12, 2023, fromrealestate.withgoogle.com/bayview/#/solutions/circular-resources

Google. (n.d.). ***Healthy Workplaces: Pushing the envelope on designing healthy workspaces that inspire.*** Retrieved May 12, 2023, from realestate.withgoogle.com/bayview/#/solutions/healthy-workplaces

Melton, P. and N. Malin. (2023, February 7). ***Google Goes Public with Ambitious Carpet Tile Standard.*** Building Green. www.buildinggreen.com/blog/google-goes-public-ambitious-carpet-tile-standard

Pichai, S. (2020, September 14). ***Our third decade of climate action: Realizing a carbon-free future.*** Google. blog.google/outreach-initiatives/sustainability/our-third-decade-climate-action-realizing-carbon-free-future/

Puettmann, M., Pierobon, F., Ganguly, I., Gu, H., Chen, C., Liang, S., Jones, S., Maples, I., & Wishnie, M. (2021). Comparative LCAs of Conventional and Mass Timber Buildings in Regions with Potential for Mass Timber Penetration. ***Sustainability 2021, 13, 13987.*** corrim.org/wp-content/uploads/2021/12/sustainability-13-13987-v2.pdf

Sparandara, L. (n.d.). ***Healthy Materials and Regenerative Design.*** Google. realestate.withgoogle.com/bayview/#/interviews/healthy-materials-and-regenerative-design

Sparandara, L., Werner, M., Kaminsky, A., Finch, L., & Douglas. K. (2019). ***Accelerating the Circular Economy through Commercial Deconstruction and Reuse.*** Google & Ellen MacArthur Foundation. www.gstatic.com/gumdrop/sustainability/google-deconstruction-and-reuse.pdf

A Regenerative Built Environment Starts with Intentional Material Design

Christina Raab

Design is a force for positive change, not only in architecture but also for innovating materials and products in the built environment.

When I started my journey in sustainability two decades ago, considering design impacts in mainstream product development and manufacturing was rare. Nowadays it is more understood that decisions made early in the design stage determine the material life cycle and sustainability of a building product. Design has the power to prevent the creation of waste and pollution right at the start and to drive innovation that positively impacts the future of our planet and society. Because materials are ubiquitous, forming the fabric of our built environment, we have a paramount opportunity to examine how the innovation of building materials can help us future-proof how we build, renovate and live.

Thoughtful design enables manufacturers and specifiers to optimize health and climate benefits, plan for disassembly and reuse, and avoid harms right from the start.
Photo: Tandem X Visuals/Unsplash

During the past several years, I have witnessed an accelerated uptake of circular design approaches in many categories and applications of building materials. These efforts mainly center on lowering the use of raw materials, reducing waste generation, and addressing the greenhouse gas emissions of the industry. Designers and manufacturers are turning to reduced virgin content, recycled or renewable resources, and materials with a lower carbon footprint. They are also designing and making building products for longevity, adaptability, and disassembly. Such approaches are essential and commendable, but they are only a stepping stone towards a future that is healthy, equitable and regenerative.

Today, frontrunning design practitioners and companies that manufacture and sell building materials understand that a more holistic approach to product innovation is required. This process often starts with intentionally designing out hazardous and polluting materials from the outset. This means optimizing the chemical and material composition of building products to assure that they are safe for people and the planet. Using healthier material inputs from the beginning also ensures that products are of better quality and are well placed for repeated and safe reuse in a circular system.

A more recent but future-defining development in the built environment has been to apply just and equitable principles in the design and production of building products. This means not only upholding fair business and labor practices within operations and supply chains, but also including diverse perspectives in the design process, which can help assure equity in use and wider accessibility of the solutions.

To achieve the ultimate paradigm shift to a future-proof material economy, however, we need a breakthrough in regenerative practices. Our designed environment has a deep effect on natural resources and our living ecosystems. Regeneration calls

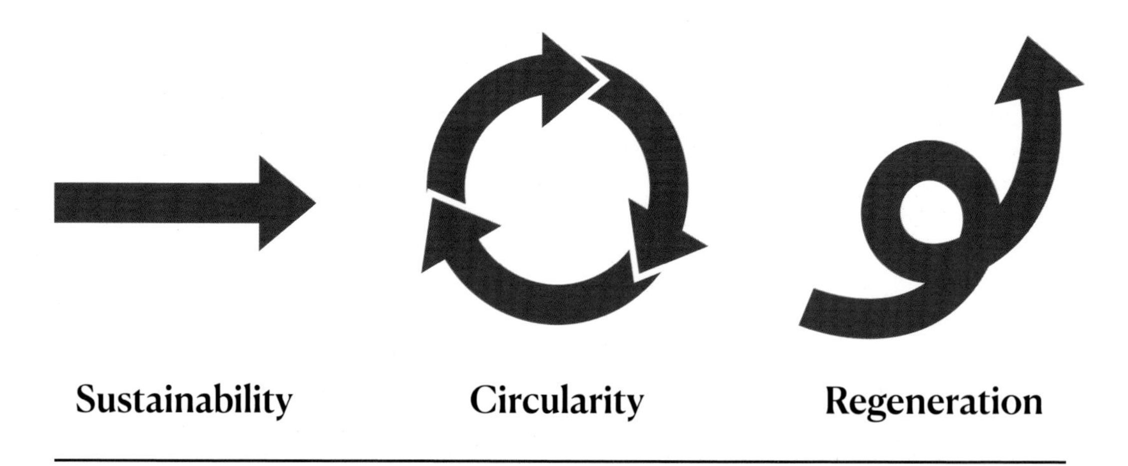

Figure 1. Designing the materials economy of tomorrow will require advancing beyond sustainability.

Nature, by default, is regenerative. In practice, regenerative design requires applying integrated thinking and considering the linkages between design, production, use and end-of-use of materials.

Photo: ANGHI/iStock

for a deeper integration with nature and a mindset shift from doing less harm to doing more good, ultimately giving more back than we take. The result will be a built environment that more closely parallels the resource cycles and material composition found in the natural environment. This starts with designing for regenerative outcomes and creating the conditions for nature to thrive. For example, bio-based materials such as timber, hemp, or straw are used in successive cycles through different applications before being safely returned to the earth. Moreover, regenerative materials have not only net zero but net positive and restorative impacts on natural systems, biodiversity, water, and climate.

Nature, by default, is regenerative. In practice, regenerative design requires applying integrated thinking and considering the linkages between design, production, use and end-of-use of materials. This often sparks a different type of innovation, one where solutions are created with a systemic lens. It also requires a much closer collaboration among stakeholders in the system: designers and architects, product manufactures, building developers, and infrastructure providers, amongst others. Changing the system can only be effective as a collective exercise and when it leans on the interdisciplinary expertise of players from across the value chain.

It takes genuine leadership and bold action to design a materials economy for tomorrow. The current state of our world and the daunting environmental and social impacts of the building and construction sector demand nothing less. Today's frontrunners see the urgent challenges of our times as opportunities and innovation by design as a solution. Despite these improvements, to catalyze the paradigm shift we must address a crucial question: how do we move from sporadic action to making healthy and regenerative materials the norm?

To begin with, regeneration must be intentional and placed front and center in product design strategies. Regeneration becomes specifically impactful when it is put in context and combined with climate and circularity goals of manufacturers and specifiers. Current design approaches are often still too compartmentalized and do not sufficiently build on the interdependence of nature-related topics such as water and energy resources, biodiversity or climate protection. Such a comprehensive design approach drives a net-positive impact on our natural systems.

Secondly, any building material innovation must consider the entire life cycle of a product and process. Only with such a holistic mindset can meaningful optimization

Photo: Josh Olalde/Unsplash

and progress happen. Practically, this means not only considering the needs of the user of the building material but focusing also on the system in which the design will exist. This might require forming novel and at times unlikely partnerships for action across the upstream and downstream value chain in order to drive benefits for the entire system. Leading designers and manufacturers make it a practice to engage in regular dialogue with system stakeholders for continued improvement and innovation of building materials.

And lastly, we have to rethink and redefine the value of materials. This is where the circular mindset comes in. We should retain only those materials that have been designed for a safe circulation and view them as a perpetual asset for a regenerative economy. Regeneration carries a widened scope of value creation where materials are key to a restored, renewed or revitalized ecosystem.

Design is at the heart of every material, product and system around us. Every transformation begins with a deliberate decision to design a different reality. By bringing design to the core of innovation and to the collaborations within the building and construction sector, a healthy, regenerative and equitable materials economy becomes not only possible but moves rapidly within our reach.

Dr. Christina Raab is a transformational leader at the interface of sustainability, circular economy and innovation. She served as President & CEO of the Cradle to Cradle Products Innovation Institute, where she powered the shift to a circular economy through market transformation and standard-setting activities. She worked closely with product manufacturers, architects & designers and project developers & owners to deploy circular and regenerative strategies in the design, production and specification of building materials. Prior Christina held leading positions at forefront multi-stakeholder initiatives and consulting firms, where she worked internationally with a variety of private sectors, multi-lateral organizations and public institutions to advance the integration of environmental and social sustainability in core business practices and across global value chains. She started her professional journey at the United Nations Industrial Development Organization and holds a PhD in materials chemistry.

Building the Map I Needed: A Common Materials Platform

Alex Muller

I entered the world of materials as a graduate student at Purdue University. The university was attempting Living Building certification for a residential building for researchers on a biological reserve. My job, which I desperately sought out, was to seek out products that disclosed their substances and met the Living Building Challenge Red List, at a time when product transparency was new and manufacturers were more resistant to the concept.

"I heard the Materials Petal is the hardest part," said the university's Sustainability Director, reflecting on my overeager request to participate. "We could probably pay a graduate student to provide support on that." I was thrilled. Reality quickly set in.

I had no idea how to put together a building, where to start searching for materials, or how to interpret what I was finding in a meaningful way, and perhaps the only person more lost than me was...the architect. I was alone in my mission,

confused, lost, and newly horrified by the inadequacies of chemical regulation in the United States.

The Purdue team eventually set and achieved a more reasonable first target of Zero Carbon. I moved to Seattle to work for the International Living Future Instituite (ILFI), where I wrote my thesis on transparency in building products, perhaps in an effort to better understand why I had struggled so much in my given task. So much has changed since that time in our efforts to identify, prioritize, and specify "healthier" materials. But despite almost a decade of action and the development of many new tools and resources, too much has stayed the same.

The more I learn about materials, the more complex their impacts become — and the greater urgency we see to shift their place in sustainability from the periphery to foundational. I have spent the last ten years of my career listening to individuals from across the building industry — from big companies and little ones, those new and old materials — in an effort to better understand why, despite so much action, there has been very little forward momentum to make all buildings healthier for people and planet.

A DESIRE FOR IMPACT

At the time of this writing, in early 2023, the building industry has been working on scaling the manufacturing and adoption of "sustainable" building materials for decades.

Yet, what is perhaps most notable is what has not changed since my time as a graduate student. Somehow, no matter the number of platforms, certifications, databases, pledges, or other market initiatives that arise, meaningful adoption of sustainable materials is still limited to a relatively small set of companies. It is still too difficult to find products that meet the Red List, let alone balance that with the many other facets of sustainability.

Materials are still considered the most complicated, time-consuming component of many green building certifications. And building certifications are, for many architecture firms or owners, the only time that materials are taken seriously as a sustainability strategy. The holistic embodied impacts of materials thus remain, on the whole, too easy to ignore and too difficult to pay attention to for most companies, and too complex to make decisions on beyond a single attribute.

I have seen countless presentations that predict that the materials industry will tidily follow the diffusion of innovation curve, with innovators at the helm leading the charge and making it easier for everyone else. For years, innovators have been leading. So why aren't sustainable materials...diffusing?

At mindful MATERIALS, our theory for why this has not happened is deceptively simple: we have been working in siloes within and across professions. Without first aligning the foundations of the ask, the market has been sent conflicting signals, dispersing the momentum leaders seek to create.

In short — long before my time at Purdue, and to this day — we have all been wandering around individually relearning the same information and re-creating the same tools to understand materials sustainability, certifications, and the impact of our decisions.

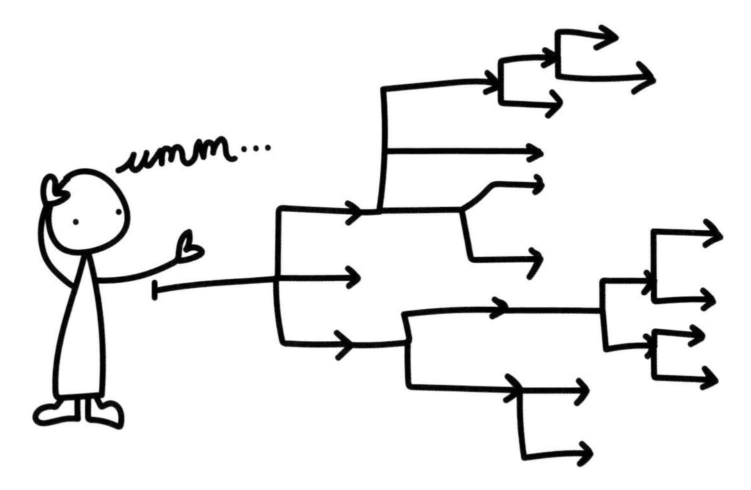

COMMITMENT TO ACT

In recent years, we have been encouraged by large-scale pledges to address materials' impacts popping up across the building industry. This level of public, shared commitment to reducing the embodied impacts of buildings was inconceivable only a few years ago.

From the AIA A&D Materials Pledge to the Interior Design Pledge for Positive Impact; from the Manufacturer Materials Commitment to the Lighting Advocacy Letter, and beyond, companies are publicly demonstrating their desire to act meaningfully and recognizing the interconnected nature of their decisions and their success.

These pledges were conceived as unifying forces within and across stakeholder groups. Each references roughly the same "buckets" of materials sustainability goals originated by the AIA Pledge: making and specifying products that address Human Health, Climate Health, Ecosystem Health, Social Health + Equity, and which support a Circular Economy. For the first time in the building industry, something approximating a common language for material sustainability is living in the minds, libraries, and sustainability strategies of firms and organizations. But it is not enough.

To uphold their pledge commitments, the companies and entities with the most resources have created their own systems, tools, resources, and pathways. These independent actions have been incredibly valuable in some ways, encouraging organizations and companies to dive deep and push forward critical areas of knowledge. However, these positive acts of sustainability demand are fracturing the market. No one is speaking the same underlying language: climate health never means the same thing twice; "PFAS-free" is unclear and inconsistent — the list goes on.

The gap between the knowledge leaders — with their teams of internal toxicologists and material experts — and the rest of us is ever-widening.. The proliferation of labels, approaches, and standards is sowing confusion and frustration among practitioners, creating extra work for manufacturers, and leading to decision paralysis for designers and purchasers.

The Pledges

Without a common language or foundation, these independent acts dissipate momentum and send conflicting signals to the market, whereas conscious alignment around common ground accelerates momentum. We need such alignment at a fundamental, unprecedented level, or else we risk squandering the positive intentions held and actions taken by so many industry players.

While pledges give us the North Star to name the outcomes we want, what we really need is a map with a consistent set of landmarks that we can all reference to find our way. That map is the Common Materials Framework (CMF).

A SHARED MAP

The Common Materials Framework is an attempt to establish common definitions for building material sustainability attributes. It allows you to connect a desire for impact, or a specific type of impact, with the materials you select and the certifications they hold.

The Common Materials Framework was developed in 2021, when mindful MATERIALS convened a Content Advisory Board and Content Working Group of cross-sector materials sustainability experts. It was the most detailed cross-stakeholder industry effort to date. For six months, this group met weekly to analyze and organize over 100 of the most common building product and material certifications and disclosures, mapping each detail to the five buckets of health and sustainability,

The Five Buckets

reflecting the five broad categories first identified in the AIA A&D Materials Pledge.

The Common Materials Framework extracts over 600 individual data points and associates them with the five pledge buckets, breaking out these factor-level impacts from their eco-labels and tying them directly to real-world impacts.

Picture two converging spider maps. On the left side, we define the categories of impact within each "bucket," the continuum of improvement, and the data points that live within each. Then, on the other side, we take each certification, break it down to its granular data points (what does it actually measure, certify, or verify), and match those up with the categories on the left. Applying that framework to products that have disclosed information in a digital format, this matching process allows anyone to quickly and easily identify which product certifications and documentations can demonstrate contributions to their sustainability goals.

While dissecting and organizing data points may not sound groundbreaking at first, this framework is the foundation for advancement and adoption that the market has been missing for decades. Since the time of its development, the CMF has been reviewed by over a dozen leading certifying bodies and data partners, and work has begun to take it beyond spreadsheet form into an interactive platform that enables users to search for products by their impacts, not just by their green labels.

Just as eco-labels and certifications have proliferated, so too have databases and workflow tools that enable practitioners to select and incorporate products with these attributes into their work. But any database is only as good as the data set that it is built upon. As the work continues to digitize and activate product sustainability data represented within the CMF, taking it from analog form and making it accessible, measurable, and searchable, we have the opportunity to streamline the flow of this information, reducing redundant data entry on the part of manufacturers and making it consistent and cohesive across all major databases and workflow tools. This consistency in data will finally allow for the enhanced functionality needed for procurement tools, ESG scoring, benchmarking, and industry-wide embodied impact measurement. The Common Materials Framework does not set these metrics; it makes them possible.

GOING FORWARD, TOGETHER

I have spent countless hours of my life watching and giving presentations that attempt to show the similarities and differences between product standards. I've been asked more times than I can remember if I have a graphic that shows the differences between all of them, and where to start if you're looking for materials that impact ecosystem health. While it's not particularly how I'd like to spend my time, the bigger point is that it clearly indicates to me that there's a whole lot of confusion out there, with even more unnecessary, redundant work being done.

We cannot scale our work, reach building professionals in their day-to-day efforts, and ultimately transform the built environment without a common definition of what makes a sustainable building product.

If we can integrate the Common Materials Framework and its associated resources everywhere product decisions are being made — all major product databases, internal firm systems, and workflow tools — it will answer all of these questions about the qualities of materials, and many more, simply because it gives us all the same map. We will all take different journeys to create change. You may use your preferred certifications or prioritize different aspects of sustainability. The Common Materials

The disconnect of mindless materials in the built environment

UNDERSTANDING THE COMMON MATERIALS FRAMEWORK

The industry has seen such a proliferation of disconnected standards and certifications — there are so many paths from which to choose — that our biggest challenge is knowing where to start and which direction to head.

The Common Materials Framework gives us such a map. And if we all use it, then your journey — and Google's journey, and Princeton's journey, and anyone else's — can be benchmarked and understood within the same framework. In this way, everyone's actions will contribute to an aligned signal that spurs the kind of exciting innovations we need.

The CMF incorporates 150 certifications and over 650 data points. Think of each of these data points as a location on that map, allowing the user to connect intent to impact, certifications to data points, and data to outcomes.

At the highest level, the CMF categorizes product impacts by the five "buckets" of the AIA Materials Pledge: Human Health, Climate Health, Ecosystem Health, Social Health and Equity, and Circular Economy . Across these five buckets, 18 sub-buckets are identified which address both product-specific and company-wide impacts, namely,

Transparency: Identify + disclose impacts
Assessment: Leverage that data to identify improvement opportunities
Commitments: Turn those opportunities into meaningful plans or improvements
Optimization: Demonstrate achievement of an existing benchmark

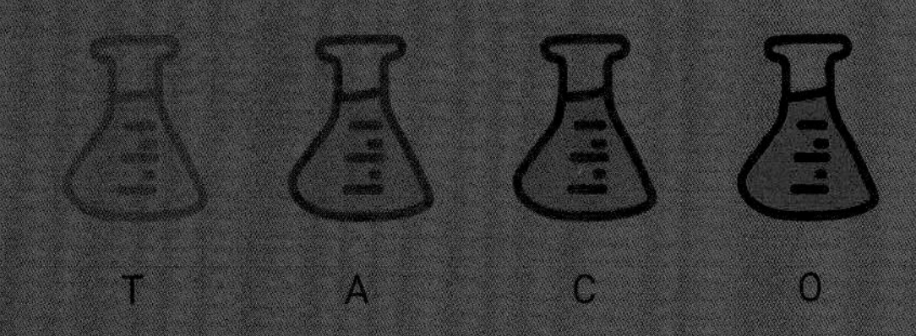

The CMF then provides relevant ways of evaluating the quality of Transparency, Assessment, Commitments, or Optimization. For example, within Substances, transparency is typically evaluated by one of these metrics: Granularity of Disclosure (ppm); Percent Disclosure; and Third-Party Verification.

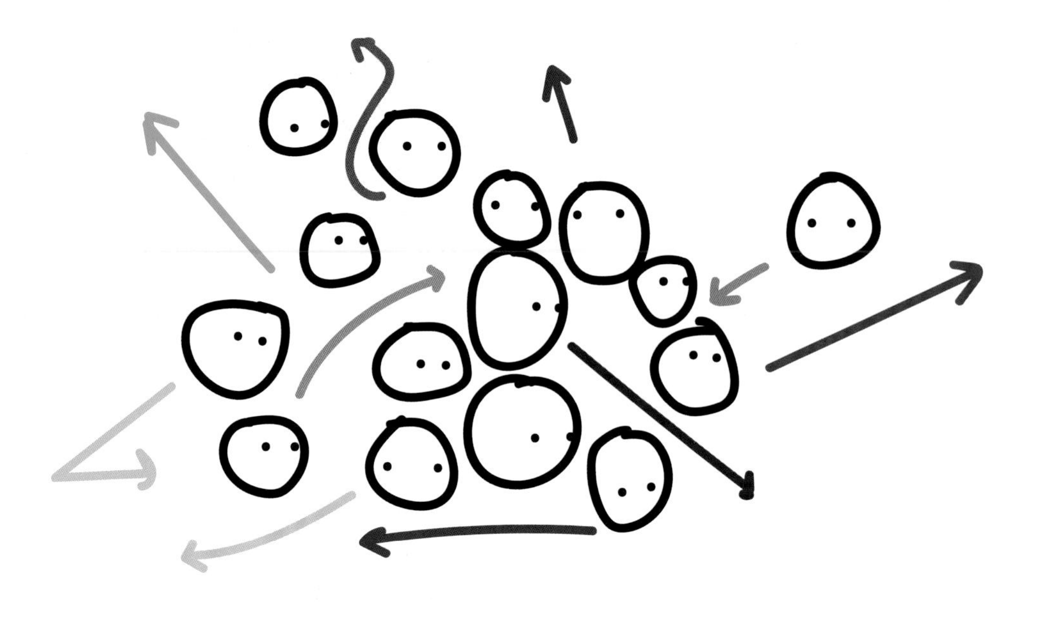

Framework makes that acceptable, allowing all of that work to be comparable, align in meaningful ways, and contribute towards a common good.

This common map helps to bridge the gap between those brave innovators and the people waiting on the other side of the knowledge chasm, unsure if they can make the jump. It gives building certifications an external point of reference around which to align their materials requirements. It gives industry materials pledges a common definition. In its own way, it seeks to bring together and amplify the work of every other contributor in this book, by contextualizing those actions in the same framework.

The story of materials only becomes more complicated the more we learn, and our desire for impact only grows. We are on the cusp of breaking through key barriers that have been holding the industry back. But the only way we will create the scale of change needed is if we do it together.

Alex Muller is the VP of Strategy and Marketing for mindful MATERIALS, Inc., a non-profit organization in the built environment seeking to inspire, motivate, and empower everyone to choose materials that prioritize health holistically. She has a background in biology and sustainability and cut her teeth in the building materials industry working on ILFI's Product Certification programs. Her work leverages illustration, humor, and storytelling to raise awareness of the connections between our everyday material choices and the broader challenges we face as individuals and a global society.

The story of materials only becomes more complicated the more we learn, and our desire for impact only grows. We are on the cusp of breaking through key barriers that have been holding the industry back. But the only way we will create the scale of change needed is if we do it together.

If we succeed in the next phase of this work, our initiatives and those of our many partners, collaborators, and co-conspirators will make a permanent shift in the market for sustainability. If we succeed, it will not be thanks to a single tool, certification, database, organization, or leader, but rather by bringing them all together and aligning them for impact.

mindful MATERIALS, INC.

mindful MATERIALS Inc. is a 501(c)(3) tax-exempt organization, dedicated to reducing, and ultimately reversing, the embodied impacts of the built environment through our collective material choices. mindful MATERIALS furthers its mission through a global cross-sector collaboration hubs, whose members convene to share learning and drive better materials decisions around an industry-aligned common materials framework for health, sustainability, and resilience. That framework will live in our curated materials Portal and be broadly integrated into industry tools, platforms, resources, education, and advocacy.

The Essential-use Approach: Putting Businesses Ahead of the Curve in Selecting Healthy Materials

Carol Kwiatkowski

Retailers, purchasers, product developers, owners, builders, and specifiers have many reasons to choose healthier products and materials. Decisions may be driven by environmental concerns, customer demand, employee health, business risk avoidance, regulatory compliance, and more. Increasingly, businesses are going above and beyond environmental regulations, working to remove chemicals of concern from their products and purchases before they are required to do so.

By applying the "essential-use" screen, businesses can avoid contributing to the proliferation of harmful chemicals in our buildings and in the greater environment. Photo: Damir Kopezhanov/Unsplash

This approach is of critical importance, as it's impossible for regulatory agencies with limited budgets to stay on top of assessing the potential hazards of tens of thousands of chemicals in commerce. In most cases, chemicals are assumed to be safe until they are proven otherwise, and it can take decades for the federal government to fully assess harm from even a single chemical. As a result, many harmful chemicals slip through the system.

In a recent paper (Balan, et al. 2023), my colleagues and I proposed a new twist on an old concept that has the potential to allow governments and businesses to move forward much more rapidly to remove harmful chemicals and protect people, wildlife, and our indoor and outdoor environments.

The essential-use approach states that chemicals of concern should be used only when their function in specific products is necessary for health, safety, or the functioning of society, and when there are no safer alternatives. This approach was first used successfully as part of the Montreal Protocol to remove harmful ozone-depleting substances such as chlorofluorocarbons.

Figure 1. Databases of Safer Chemicals and Products by Sector

Sector	Organization and Database Name*
CLEANING PRODUCTS	US Environmental Protection Agency: Safer Choice
BUILDING MATERIALS AND FURNITURE	International Living Future Institute: Declare Healthy Building Network: Home Free Mindful Materials: Portal Center for Environmental Health: Healthier Furniture Purchasing Guide BIFMA: Level Certified Furniture Products
ELECTRONICS	Global Electronics Council: EPEAT Registry TCO Certified: Product Finder
PERSONAL CARE PRODUCTS	Environmental Working Group: Skin Deep
TEXTILES	ZDHC: Gateway
FOOD PACKAGING	Food Packaging Forum: Brand and Retailer Initiatives
MULTI-SECTOR	Cradle to Cradle: Certified Products GreenScreen Certified: Products
CHEMICALS	ChemForward: SAFER ChemSec: Marketplace

More recently, the European Union proposed phasing out per-and polyfluoroalkyl substances (PFAS) and other harmful chemicals except for uses that are essential for society.

Businesses can also apply the approach to their lists of chemicals of concern, such as Restricted Substance Lists. Our proposed strategy identifies three key questions that could be asked by anyone in charge of choosing materials or products. The key to the strategy is asking the easiest questions first.

The most obvious question is whether there are safer alternatives available. Keep in mind that this is not a one-time effort. Safer alternatives are being developed all the time and the more we demand them, the more will be developed. Many resources are available for businesses to identify safer chemicals and products.

A more challenging question is whether the use of a chemical of concern is justified because such use is necessary for health, safety, or the functioning of society. If not, its use should be discontinued. Examples of non-essential uses include chemicals such as PFAS in children's toys, cosmetics, and many clothing applications.

In my opinion, one of the most interesting questions is whether the chemical provides an essential function. Surprisingly, sometimes you can simply stop using the chemical, or request that your supplier stop using it, without loss of performance. Here's one example.

KEEN Footwear began applying the essential-use approach when they made a commitment to eliminate all PFAS from their footwear. The first step was to identify all the uses of PFAS in their footwear — they were quite surprised to find over 100 different ones! Relatively quickly they were able to determine that 70 percent of the uses did not provide a necessary function, so they removed them. Then they focused on evaluating the remaining uses and finding safer substitutes, eventually removing all uses of PFAS. KEEN also took the unusual step of sharing their process publicly, and they even issued a challenge to other outdoor gear companies to do the same.

Santa Monica City Hall East, a Living Building in Los Angeles County, restricted materials that include Red List chemicals. Photo: courtesy Amber Richane

In our paper on essential uses, we highly recommend sharing information about chemical uses, safer alternatives, and essential-use determinations. This tactic reduces redundancy, saves time and money, and expedites decision-making for others. Aligning decisions on which uses are essential avoids confusion within the supply chain and among customers and protects people in different regions from having harmful chemical production move from one place to another. Sharing also gives large and small businesses, imports, exports, and online markets access to the same information. When the goal is to protect health and the environment, choosing cooperation over competition serves the greater good.

At our Institute, we have put considerable effort into determining if certain functions of chemicals are necessary. Three examples of non-essential uses of chemicals of concern are organohalogen flame retardants (OHFR), PFAS, and quaternary ammonium compounds (QACs).

For decades and across the nation, toxic OHFRs were added to furniture foam and children's products to meet the California Furniture Flammability Standard (TB 117). Our review of the relevant

Photo: Kam Idris/Unsplash

Aligning decisions on which uses are essential avoids confusion within the supply chain and among customers, and protects people in different regions from having harmful chemical production move from one place to another.

literature demonstrated that furniture with TB117-compliant foam did not prevent ignitions from small flame sources; nor did it significantly reduce fire severity (Babrauskas, et al., 2011). After years of effort by many organizations engaging in advocacy and policy work, conducting scientific research, and meeting with trade associations, TB117 was revised, and now OHFRs and other harmful flame retardants are no longer used in most North American furniture.

More recently, we published the results of a study demonstrating that PFAS are minimally effective in preventing stains and providing water and oil repellency in furniture fabrics (LaPier et al., 2023). PFAS are associated with numerous health harms, including cancer, liver damage, obesity, infertility, reduced response to vaccines, and more severe COVID-19 outcomes. These chemicals of concern are used in thousands of consumer and industrial products for a variety of functions which have been marketed to seem essential. If not for a few environmentally conscious businesses who suggested PFAS might not perform as advertised, we might never have conducted our study. In addition to uses in furniture, our findings call into question the essentiality of other PFAS uses that have likely never been studied to demonstrate their touted effectiveness.

A third example comes from chemicals known as QACs, which are widely used in cleaning products, personal care products, and durable consumer goods for their antimicrobial and other properties. Use of QACs has increased in recent years in response to the COVID-19 pandemic. For some uses, such as hospital furniture, the effectiveness of QACs at preventing disease transmission has yet to be demonstrated (Schettler, 2016, 2020). Given their known effects on antimicrobial resistance and increasing evidence of health harms, our recent paper recommends that non-essential uses be restricted (Arnold, et. al., 2023) — for example, general cleaning, where disinfection is not needed, or where the effectiveness of QACs has not been demonstrated.

Avoiding chemicals of concern by applying the essential-use approach may be easier than you think. The only justification for continuing to use harmful chemicals is when all three of these statements are true:

1. The function of the chemical in the product is necessary;
2. The use is essential to health, safety or the functioning of society; and
3. There are no safer alternatives.

Photo: Roberto Nickson/Unsplash

Importantly, the designation of "essential" is temporary. Chemical uses are only essential until a safer alternative is developed.

There are many benefits to the essential-use approach. One is that it can be applied to large classes of harmful chemicals, as demonstrated in our examples. This helps avoid what are called "regrettable substitutions" — where a harmful chemical is replaced by a similar one from the same class that has yet to be thoroughly studied. Unfortunately, it can take decades for a regrettable substitute to be identified and restricted, and countless people (and the environment) may be harmed in the interim.

The essential-use approach also promotes the development of safer alternatives. If purchasers stop buying harmful chemicals,

REFERENCES

Arnold, W. A., Blum, A., Branyan, J., Bruton, T. A., Carignan, C. C., Cortopassi, G., Datta, S., DeWitt, J., Doherty, A. C., Halden, R. U. Harari, H., Hartmann, E. M., Hrubec, T. C., Iyer, S. Kwiatkowski, C. F., LaPier, J., Li, D., Li, L., Muñiz Ortiz, J. G., Salamova, A., Schettler, T., Seguin, R. P. Soehl, A., Sutton, R. Xu, L., Zheng, G. (2023). Quaternary Ammonium Compounds: A Chemical Class of Emerging Concern. ***Environmental Science & Technology*** (in press).

Babrauskas, V., Blum, A., Daley, R., & Birnbaum, L. (2011). Flame retardants in furniture foam: benefits and risks. ***Fire Safety Science, 10, 265-278.*** doi.org/10.3801/IAFSS.FSS.10-265

Bălan, S. A., Andrews, D. Q., Blum A., Diamond, M. L., Rojello Fernández, S., Harriman, E., Lindstrom, A. B., Reade, A., Richter, L., Sutton, R., Wang, Z., & Kwiatkowski, C. F. (2023). Optimizing Chemicals Management in the United States and Canada through the Essential-Use Approach. ***Environmental Science & Technology 57(4)***, 1568-1575. doi.org/10.1021/acs.est.2c05932

BIFMA. ***Level. Certified Furniture Products.*** www.bifma.org/mpage/levelcertifiedproducts (accessed April 26, 2023)

Center for Environmental Health. ***Healthier Furniture Purchasing Guide.***. docs.google.com/spreadsheets/d/1GNHY84rgGX7rxgWg7ukYWZWBx8bVu43_ONAMAHlnngl/edit#gid=1163922567 (accessed April 26, 2023)

ChemForward. ***SAFER.*** www.chemforward.org/safer-alternatives (accessed April 26, 2023)

ChemSec. ***Marketplace.*** marketplace.chemsec.org (accessed April 26, 2023)

Cradle to Cradle. ***Certified Products.*** c2ccertified.org/certified-products-and-materials (accessed April 26, 2023)

Environmental Working Group. ***Skin Deep.*** www.ewg.org/skindeep (accessed April 26, 2023)

Food Packaging Forum. ***Brand and Retailer Initiatives.*** www.foodpackagingforum.org/brand-retailer-initiatives (accessed April 26, 2023)

Global Electronics Council. ***EPEAT Registry.*** www.epeat.net/search-computers-and-displays (accessed April 26, 2023)

GreenScreen Certified. ***Products.*** www.greenscreenchemicals.org/certified/products (accessed April 26, 2023)

Healthy Building Network. ***Home Free: Your Roadmap to Healthier Materials.*** homefree.healthybuilding.net (accessed April 26, 2023)

International Living Future Institute. ***Declare. The Nutrition Label for Products.*** declare.living-future.org (accessed April 26, 2023)

manufacturers will put more effort into developing safer products and processes.

By addressing the low-hanging fruit quickly, we can free up resources for the most challenging decisions, such as how to waterproof personal protective equipment (a currently essential use of PFAS for some products). Most of all, the essential-use approach can remove many uses quickly, without waiting for the regulatory system to catch up with all the untested and potentially harmful chemicals already on the market.

The business community has a huge opportunity to clean up the environment and protect the health of people and wildlife by applying the essential-use approach to chemicals of concern. We look forward to seeing the change.

Carol Kwiatkowski, PhD, is a Science and Policy Senior Associate at the Green Science Policy Institute. She is also an Adjunct Assistant Professor at North Carolina State University. At the Institute, she leads research projects associated with the "Six Classes" of harmful chemicals: PFAS, flame retardants, antimicrobials, bisphenols & phthalates, organic solvents, and certain metals. Prior to joining GSPI, Dr. Kwiatkowski served for eleven years as Executive Director of The Endocrine Disruption Exchange, a science-based non-profit organization focusing on the impacts of environmental chemicals on hormone disruption.

LaPier, J., Blum, A., Brown, B. R., Kwiatkowski, C. F., Phillips, B., Ray, H., & Sun, G. (2023). Evaluating the Performance of Per- and Polyfluoroalkyl Substance Finishes on Upholstery Fabrics. ***AATCC Journal of Research 0(0).*** doi.org/10.1177/24723444231159856

Mindful Materials. ***Portal.*** portal.mindfulmaterials.com (accessed April 26, 2023)

Schettler, T. Antimicrobials in Hospital Furnishings: Do They Help Reduce Healthcare-Associated Infections? (2016). ***Healthcare Without Harm.*** noharm-uscanada.org/sites/default/files/documents-files/3854/Antimicrobials%20Report%202016_1.pdf. (accessed 2023-04-26).

Schettler, T. Antimicrobials in Hospital Furnishings: Do They Help Combat COVID-19? (2020). ***Healthcare Without Harm.*** noharm-uscanada.org/sites/default/files/documents-files/6513/Antimicrobials%20and%20COVID-19%20-%20August%202020.pdf. (accessed 2023-04-26)

TCO Certified. ***Product Finder.*** tcocertified.com/product-finder (accessed April 26, 2023)

US Environmental Protection Agency. ***Safer Choice.*** www.epa.gov/saferchoice/products (accessed April 26, 2023)

ZDHC. ***Gateway.*** www.zdhc-gateway.com (accessed April 26, 2023)

GREEN SCIENCE POLICY INSTITUTE

The Green Science Policy Institute is nonprofit with a mission to protect human and ecological health by facilitating the safer use of chemicals. We work with business, government, academic, and public interest groups to develop innovative solutions for reducing harmful chemicals in products. We collaborate with leading scientists on policy-relevant research projects and translate scientific information to educate decision makers, the press, and the public. Since its founding, our Institute has contributed to preventing the use of "Six Classes" of harmful chemicals in consumer products and building materials worldwide.

Lessons from Tech Can Accelerate the Transformation to a Healthier Built Environment

Wendy Vittori

Imagine if the products we use to construct, finish, and furnish buildings could change at the same pace as products based on information technology?

In 1965, Gordon Moore, one of the founders of the Intel Corporation, predicted that the number of components on an integrated circuit, aka "chip," would double every year. His forecast held for ten years. In 1975, Moore revised his forecast to a doubling every two years. This was not based on knowing exactly how this would happen over time, but on Moore's insight that there was a solid opportunity for industry innovation to make this forecast a reality.

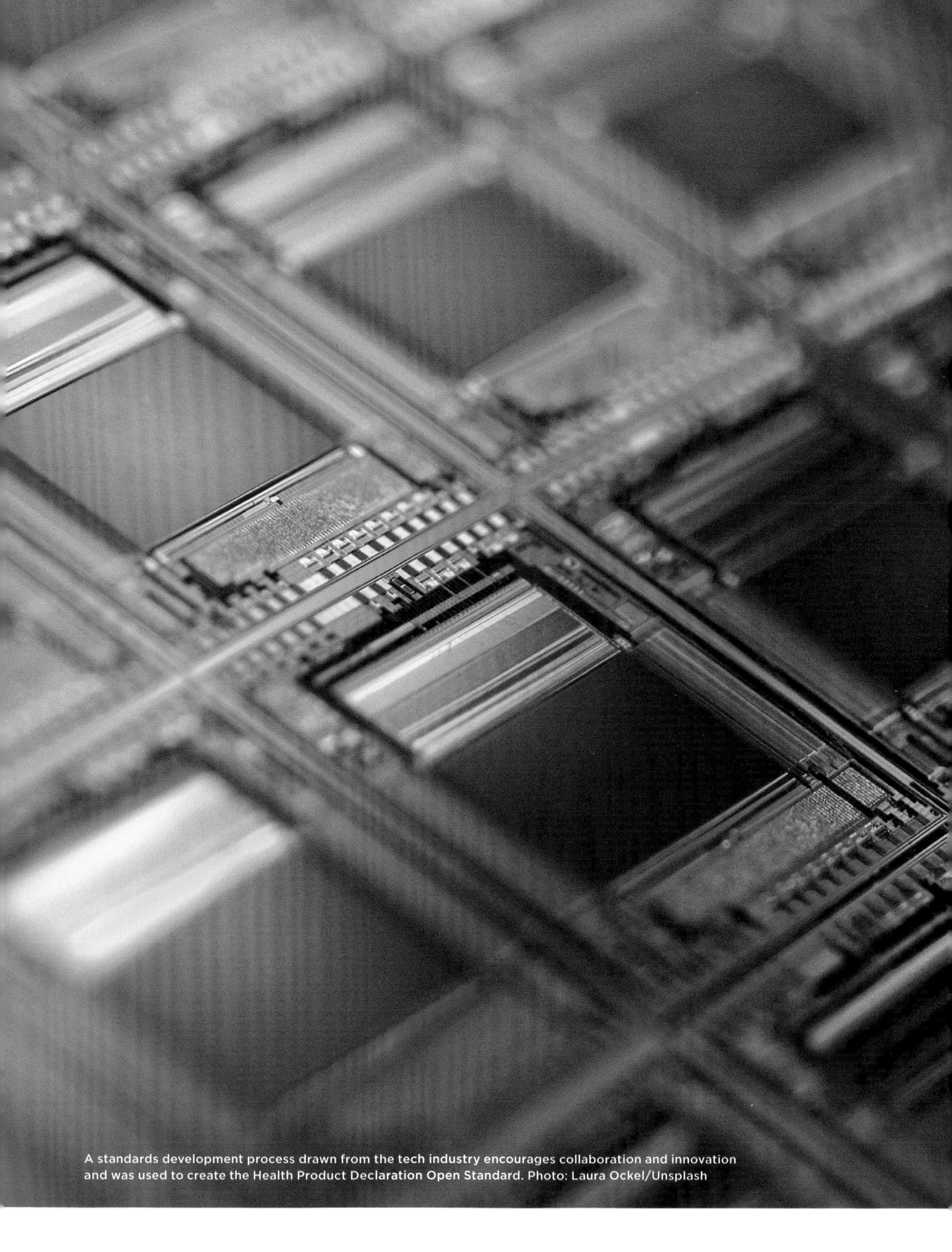

A standards development process drawn from the tech industry encourages collaboration and innovation and was used to create the Health Product Declaration Open Standard. Photo: Laura Ockel/Unsplash

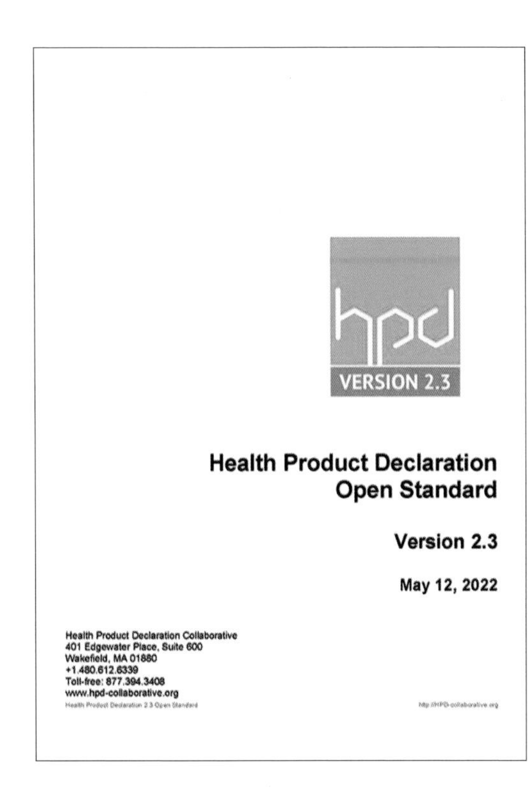

hpd
VERSION 2.3

Health Product Declaration Open Standard

Version 2.3

May 12, 2022

Health Product Declaration Collaborative
401 Edgewater Place, Suite 600
Wakefield, MA 01880
+1.480.612.6339
Toll-free: 877.394.3408
www.hpd-collaborative.org

Health Product Declaration 2.3 Open Standard

http://HPD-collaborative.org

As David Rotman observed in MIT Technology Review in 2020, "How did a simple prediction, based on extrapolating from a graph of the number of transistors by year — a graph that at the time had only a few data points — come to define a half-century of progress? *In part, at least, because the semiconductor industry decided it would*" (Rotman, 2020). To put a finishing point on this, in 1975 the most advanced chips had approximately 65,000 transistors; this number is now over 100 billion and projected to reach one trillion by 2030 (Jimenez, 2022).

Where was the discussion of building material health in 1965? Why is it, despite decades of increasingly compelling information linking product ingredients to unwanted impacts on human and environmental health, that there has been relatively limited advancement in the material health of building products?

My involvement with these questions began in 2007 when, after a long career in product development in the high-tech industry, I established a strategy consultancy with the goal of contributing the knowledge I had gained to help small organizations with transformational product development goals. I had not envisioned applying these lessons outside the high-tech world when I started. As it turned out, I connected with Bill Walsh at the Healthy Building Network (HBN). Bill had founded HBN in 2000 to reduce the use of hazardous chemicals in building products as a means of improving human health and the environment.

This is the question Bill posed to me:

Are there lessons that could be applied from the much faster pace of product innovation in the tech industry that might spur a more rapid transformation of building products to use healthier ingredients?

Looking back now at the work we initiated in 2007, I suggest the answer to Bill's question is "Yes."

We responded to this call to action by creating the Health Product Declaration® (HPD) Open Standard. Looking back at how we got started and how far we have progressed, we can better understand the opportunities we now have to accelerate the transformation of building products to include a fundamental consideration of their impacts to human and environmental health.

UNDERSTANDING THE CHALLENGE

As we embarked in 2008 on the project that became the HPD Open Standard, we first looked at the current state of innovation for developing healthier building products. We made a few observations:

1. Limited demand for healthier building products from the market — specifically, from those who select and specify the purchase of building products.

2. Lack of a shared commitment to innovate towards healthier products throughout the building products supply chain.

3. Insufficient availability of sources and quantity of capital investment to pursue material health innovation in building products.

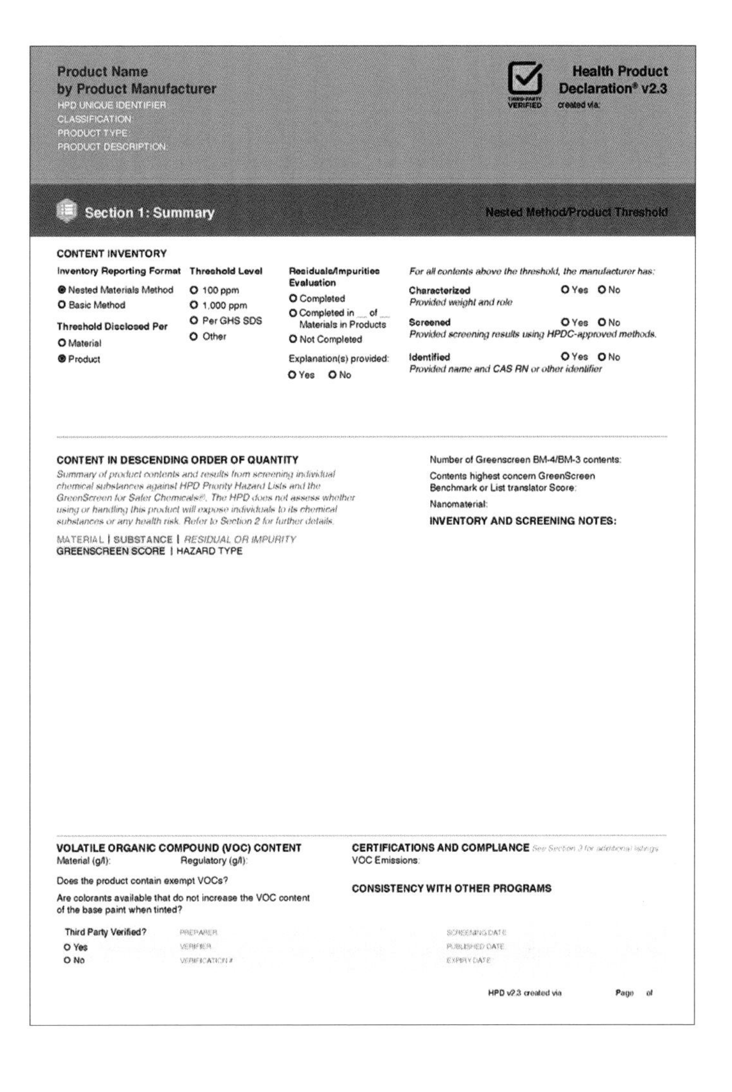
Product Name
by Product Manufacturer
HPD UNIQUE IDENTIFIER:
CLASSIFICATION:
PRODUCT TYPE:
PRODUCT DESCRIPTION:

THIRD-PARTY VERIFIED
Health Product Declaration® v2.3
created via:

Section 1: Summary
Nested Method/Product Threshold

CONTENT INVENTORY

Inventory Reporting Format
● Nested Materials Method
O Basic Method

Threshold Disclosed Per
O Material
● Product

Threshold Level
O 100 ppm
O 1,000 ppm
O Per GHS SDS
O Other

Residuals/Impurities Evaluation
O Completed
O Completed in __ of __ Materials in Products
O Not Completed

Explanation(s) provided:
O Yes O No

For all contents above the threshold, the manufacturer has:

Characterized O Yes O No
Provided weight and role

Screened O Yes O No
Provided screening results using HPDC-approved methods.

Identified O Yes O No
Provided name and CAS RN or other identifier

CONTENT IN DESCENDING ORDER OF QUANTITY
Summary of product contents and results from screening individual chemical substances against HPD Priority Hazard Lists and the GreenScreen for Safer Chemicals®. The HPD does not assess whether using or handling this product will expose individuals to its chemical substances or any health risk. Refer to Section 2 for further details.

MATERIAL | SUBSTANCE | *RESIDUAL OR IMPURITY*
GREENSCREEN SCORE | HAZARD TYPE

Number of Greenscreen BM-4/BM-3 contents:
Contents highest concern GreenScreen Benchmark or List translator Score:
Nanomaterial:
INVENTORY AND SCREENING NOTES:

VOLATILE ORGANIC COMPOUND (VOC) CONTENT
Material (g/l): Regulatory (g/l):
Does the product contain exempt VOCs?
Are colorants available that do not increase the VOC content of the base paint when tinted?

CERTIFICATIONS AND COMPLIANCE *See Section 3 for additional listings*
VOC Emissions:

CONSISTENCY WITH OTHER PROGRAMS

Third Party Verified?
O Yes
O No

PREPARER
VERIFIER
VERIFICATION #

SCREENING DATE
PUBLISHED DATE
EXPIRY DATE

HPD v2.3 created via Page of

Internal organizational factors also play an important role in innovation. Innovation — bringing new ideas to commercial reality — requires an organizational culture that supports creativity and risk taking. Leadership support is a crucial element, directing resources to support innovation projects and the risks inherent in trying something new. Without leadership support, the odds of establishing and sustaining a culture of innovation are difficult. We found that relatively few organizations in the building industry had established the cultural and leadership support needed for material health innovation in building products to take hold.

Understanding this industry and organizational context helped us understand factors that were likely contributing to the slow rate of innovation towards healthier building products.

ORGANIZING TO ACCELERATE TRANSFORMATION TO A HEALTHIER BUILT ENVIRONMENT

By 2008, a growing number of participants in the building industry — architects, designers, contractors, owners, manufacturers — were becoming interested in material health and were starting to take action. Typically, these early champions lacked training and expertise in fields such as product chemistry, toxicology, and health. For the most part, they were architects and designers learning as they went about the quite technical world of material health practice. As we spoke with them, we learned that even the most dedicated practitioners struggled to find the basic information needed to understand a building product's potential human and environmental health impacts.

- Many practitioners would first turn to a long-standing source of information about product ingredients and environmental and human health impacts: the Material Safety Data Sheet, now called the Safety Data Sheet (SDS). This report is required by the Occupational Safety and Health Administration for many manufactured products in the United States. While available for many building products, the SDS reports a product's chemical inventory at a higher threshold than is ideal for material health analysis and lacks a complete inventory of all known human and environmental health hazards.

- New tools that supported material health practitioners, such as MBDC's Cradle To Cradle® Certified Products Program, ILFI's Living Building Challenge, Building Green's Green*Spec*® and HBN's Pharos Building Products Library, had been introduced. However, because of the newness of these programs and the relatively high costs of gathering and assessing information, the number of building products for which they provided information was very small.

- Another approach that seemed promising was the Environmental Product Declaration, which includes a life cycle analysis of environmental impacts and incorporates the reporting of the product ingredients. While very useful for understanding many environmental impacts, especially energy and carbon-related metrics, the methodology used for reporting product ingredients is not ideally suited to performing a complete material health assessment, which is needed to fully understand human and environmental health impacts.

It was clear from our analysis that while a focus on the healthfulness of building products was growing and new methods were emerging, there was still much work to be done to create the foundation to support a thriving ecosystem of material health practice, let alone make doing this work easy and scalable.

As we thought about the leverage points that could help accelerate this growing movement to healthier building products, we found one key component lacking: a common language and specification for the information needed to evaluate the human and environmental health impacts

Collaboration-oriented standards are developed specifically to meet the needs of the open innovation community that wants to innovate new solutions. They are open to all, so that new participants can easily enter.

of building products. Each of the tools and methods we found — and the new ones being introduced — did this task but used different collections of data elements. A common term would be used to describe a piece of information, for example, "chemical ID," and it was generally intended to "mean" the same thing in the different methods. Yet, in practice, there could be differences in how that data element was reported, even small ones, that made it impossible to know that the information was, in fact, identical from one program to the other. These differences, and the lack of a common reference standard, also made it very difficult to apply information technology in all the ways that could help accelerate material health progress.

This is where we saw an opportunity to take a page from the tech industry playbook: introducing an "open industry standard" for a common language and specification. Such a standard could provide a strong foundation on which to build the emerging material health ecosystem.

The result was the formation and introduction in 2012 of the Health Product Declaration Open Standard. We formed an industry coalition representing all aspects of the built environment: architecture, design, construction, ownership, product manufacturers, rating and certification programs, subject matter experts in chemistry and toxicology, and others, and brought this group together in a not-for-profit, standard developing organization: the HPD Collaborative (HPDC). We adopted the standards development process — a stakeholder consensus governance model — that has enabled the rapid creation and evolution of high-impact standards, such as USB, in the tech industry.

What makes this method of standards development powerful is its focus on creating a viable platform for open, collaborative innovation of new solutions (Chesbrough, 2006). This is different from the purpose of many standards, which is to ensure outcomes are compliant with that standard as defined. Collaboration-oriented standards are developed specifically to meet the needs of the open innovation community that wants to innovate new solutions. They are open to all, so that new participants can easily enter. In contrast, many existing standards include significant barriers to entry for newcomers. In addition, the standards governance process is designed to be nimble, enable rapid feedback on how well the standard is working, add new ideas, and adapt and change to better foster and accelerate innovation.

So far, the results from the HPD initiative have been strong. As of May 2023, over 800 manufacturers have published over 11,000

HPD reports, which represent well over 40,000 individual building products and the majority of building product categories. As a measure of progress in the use of these reports by building project design teams, over 4,600 projects that are pursuing LEED certification are using the LEED Material Ingredients Disclosure and Optimization credit. Only four years ago, fewer than 1,000 projects were using this credit. The governance process for the HPD Open Standard engages over eighty industry participants who represent all aspects of the built environment. The rapid evolution of the HPD has already resulted in five revisions in the ten years since HPD Version 1.0 was introduced.

Photo: Jeridien Villegas/Unsplash

WHAT NEXT STEPS CAN WE TAKE TO ACCELERATE CHANGE FROM THIS POINT FORWARD?

Here are some next steps that we are working toward within the HPD initiative:

1. Make it easy for project teams to find and use products with material health disclosures. For businesses to invest in the product innovation that will reduce and eliminate the use of substances of concern in their products, they need to be confident that these investments will find significant market demand. In the early stages of product transformation, this can present a real problem because there are not yet enough new products to make it easy for the specifier/purchaser to find the ones that fits their needs. This is especially true in the building industry, where there are many factors project teams must consider beyond the material health of a product. It's the classic chicken-and-egg dilemma: How do we get both more products and more demand, all at the same time?

We have now progressed to a stage where, at least in some product categories, it is possible to find a significant number of products that already have some type of material health disclosure, such as an HPD, Declare label, or C2C certification. A great next step will be to make it much easier for project teams to find and use products with material health disclosures. New easy-to-use, low-cost, end-to-end solutions for building projects that link the process of discovery and specification of products with such disclosures with the other selection criteria and steps in the design/procurement/construction process are starting to become available. We need to foster their growth and success. When project teams significantly reward improved material health in their product selection, increased investment in improving building product material health will follow.

2. Innovate material health information technology solutions to meet the needs of new participants in our open, collaborative material health innovation process. With all the growth we have seen, the vast majority of potential participants — manufacturers and building project design teams — have yet to significantly adopt material health practice. Bringing new participants into material health practice requires specifically focusing on the needs of these new, potential participants. We need to retain the rigor of the disclosure methods we have developed but make the end solution much easier for someone who is not an expert in material health. We need to seamlessly integrate the back-end information technology to present a simple user interface. Doing so will require a strong commitment from the ecosystem participants to continue working together toward a common goal of widespread adoption of material health practice.

3. Streamline and simplify participation for all members of the product development and delivery supply chain. One of the greatest challenges to understanding opportunities for product innovation is gaining information about all the ingredients that go into a product. Modern supply chains have become much more outsourced, globalized, and commoditized over the past several decades. This means that the manufacturer of the end product may truly not know where the basic ingredients come from several tiers upstream in their supply chain. We need to tackle this issue by fundamentally engaging the ingredient suppliers in supporting the widespread adoption of material health practice in the building industry. We need to create incentives for their participation that align the major players in the supply chain to support material health innovation.

We want our building products and our buildings to be healthier. How do we go from being an industry that is largely acting without regard to the material health consequences of our products and buildings to one that embraces and fundamentally considers the human and environmental health consequences of our design decisions for every product, and every project? This will not be a simple change. Many factors must align for this to happen. It's going to take considerable time to make this a reality, even as we increase the rate and pace of change significantly. The classic phrase, "It's not a sprint; it's a marathon," is apt in describing the challenges to transforming to healthier building products.

Our open collaborative innovation approach is making good progress. Can we come up with something like a "Moore's Law" to help us foresee — and accelerate — the rate of that progress? If you are reading this, you are leader in our industry. *We can together decide that a healthier built environment is what we want to create. Let us make it a reality.*

Photo: pixelprof/iStock

Wendy Vittori is Executive Director of the Health Product Declaration Collaborative, a not-for-profit, member organization committed to transparency and innovation for safer and healthier building products. Prior to assuming this position in 2015, Wendy has served as a leader in business, academic and civic contributions for over thirty years. Beginning her career as a software engineer, she led technology businesses at both Intel Corporation and Motorola, Inc. In 2007, Wendy founded Vittori Consulting LLC, a strategy and organization consulting firm. She has served as a faculty associate at the ASU Nonprofit Management Institute and was assistant professor at Northeastern University College of Business in Boston, Massachusetts. She received an A.B. from Harvard College, an MBA from Northeastern University, and was a doctoral candidate and Arthur D. Little fellow at the Harvard Business School in the fields of strategic management and entrepreneurship.

THE HEALTH PRODUCT DECLARATION COLLABORATIVE

Health Product Declaration® (HPD) Collaborative is a not-for-profit, member association with over 360 organizational members, representing the full spectrum of the building industry: architects, designers, building owners, manufacturers, consultants, information systems, researchers and others who all share a common purpose: to improve the transparency of information and material health in buildings and the environment.

The HPD Open Standard is a standardized specification for the accurate, reliable, and consistent reporting of product contents and associated health information for products used in the built environment. HPDs are harmonized with programs such as International Living Future Institute, Cradle-to-Cradle Product Innovation Institute, Clean Production Action, BIFMA, LEED, WELL and many others.

REFERENCES

Chesbrough, Henry (2006). ***Open Innovation: The New Imperative for Creating and Profiting from Technology.*** Harvard Business Review. store.hbr.org/product/open-innovation-the-new-imperative-for-creating-and-profiting-from-technology/8377?sku=8377-HBK-ENG

Jimenez, Jorge. (2022, December 6). ***Intel says there will be one trillion transistors on chips by 2030.*** PC Gamer. www.pcgamer.com/intel-says-there-will-be-one-trillion-transistors-on-chips-by-2030/

Rotman, David (2020, February 24). ***We're not prepared for the end of Moore's Law.*** MIT Technology Review. www.technologyreview.com/2020/02/24/905789/were-not-prepared-for-the-end-of-moores-law/

Translating Research into Practice for a Holistic, Sustainable Built Environment

Heather Henriksen

Harvard University is working to create a sustainable built environment that addresses climate, health, and equity. Since 2009, we have had holistic sustainable building standards, co-created with our faculty, that draw upon research, science, and data.

With more than 650 buildings covering 27 million square feet of real estate, we have the unique opportunity to use the Harvard campus as a testbed to advance solutions for healthier and more sustainable building practices. This testbed is especially relevant beyond our campus because of its size and complex governance, which are similar to that of a multinational company or mid-sized city.

Harvard's new Science and Engineering Complex incorporates many sustainability features such as swales, constructed wetlands, and rooftop gardens. Metal awnings wrap and shade the building, saving valuable energy. Photo: Kristen LaFratta/ Harvard OFS

Students and staff study, relax, eat, and converge at the Susan A. and Richard F. Smith Campus Center. Photo: Kris Snibbe, Harvard Staff Photographer

Our world-class faculty, renowned researchers, and diverse student body allow us to leverage the latest multi-disciplinary research and innovation on a vast range of sustainable development topics. We are focusing our efforts through the lens of health, while also addressing climate, equity, resilience, and a circular economy for holistic solutions. Together with faculty, the Office for Sustainability initially created the Harvard Healthier Building Academy (HHBA) to reduce and eliminate the use of harmful classes of chemicals in all building projects. We use the HHBA goals, standards, and approach to advance solutions that can be replicated to expand a more sustainable built environment and healthier future at Harvard and beyond. Scaling this work is a priority linked to our mission to educate and help solve global challenges. We do this in partnership with large commercial and non-profit owners as well as manufacturers, our staff, and practitioners — including architects, engineers, and contractors — to replicate solutions.

Our world-class faculty, renowned researchers, and diverse student body allow us to leverage the latest multi-disciplinary research and innovation on a vast range of sustainable development topics.

CLIMATE CONTEXT AND CONNECTIONS TO HEALTH

After meeting its first science-based climate goal in 2016, Harvard set a goal to be fossil fuel-free by 2050, with a bridging strategy to be fossil fuel-neutral by 2026. To meet Goal Zero, Harvard must transition all fossil fuel-powered operations to clean energy sources without the use of offsets. This means two district utility plants, which are owned and operated by the university, all purchased electricity, hundreds of buildings with fossil fuel infrastructure, and our vehicle fleet cannot use fossil fuels.

Rather than focusing only on carbon emissions, we have placed health at the heart of our climate goals in order to draw attention to the full set of damages caused by our use of fossil fuels. Harvard is seeking to reduce negative health impacts associated with fossil-fuel use and production, such as the air pollution produced and upstream health and ecosystem impacts (President and Fellows of Harvard University, 2021). We are also working to reduce embodied carbon (the carbon used to make and transport products), without the use of fossil fuels.

In short, we are examining the whole life cycle of our buildings and supply chains and the impact that new construction, renovations, operations, and maintenance have on our planet. At the broadest level, we aim to reduce fossil fuels linked to the creation of emissions, plastics, and toxic chemicals — all of which encompass fossil fuels at their base — to address climate, health, and equity.

Photo: Kris Snibbe, Harvard Staff Photographer

ABOUT THE HARVARD HEALTHIER BUILDING ACADEMY

Launched in 2016, the Harvard Healthier Building Academy (HHBA) is a partnership led by the Office for Sustainability together with researchers from the Harvard T. H. Chan School of Public Health, John A. Paulson School of Engineering and Applied Sciences, and Harvard Medical School. HHBA is working to transform the marketplace of building products by identifying, tracking, and eliminating chemical classes of concern that pose health risks and, where possible, reducing other pollution and waste. HHBA has also worked with other large leading owners to translate science into practice by removing toxic chemicals from the everyday building products we all buy.

We have prioritized health as a key topic within sustainable building because this is an area where research has not been sufficiently translated into practice. Healthier buildings encompass many areas, including better indoor air quality, access to daylight, healthier building products, and biophilic design. While the HHBA is focused on comprehensive solutions, our supply chain has been a priority as purchasing decisions have an enormous impact, especially upstream, where chemicals of concern and emissions are created and used in manufacturing.

Targeting Chemicals of Concern

We believe the proliferation of toxic chemicals — used by industries to create everyday products purchased by both consumers and commercial owners — presents a serious global, systemic challenge. In the United States, there are more than 80,000 industrial chemicals on the Environmental Protection Agency's Chemical Substance Inventory, yet only a handful of these chemicals of concern are banned nationwide. Our faculty recommended focusing on a few key classes (or groups) of chemicals instead of individual lists of chemicals to avoid "regrettable substitutions," where one chemical of concern is removed and replaced with something similar.

HHBA is focused on three key classes of chemicals of concern: chemical flame retardants; antimicrobials (used for health claims); and "forever chemicals," known as per- and poly-fluoroalkyl substances (PFAS). These three classes of chemicals are often present in interior product categories like furniture, carpets, curtains, flooring, and other everyday products for our homes; they even exist in our clothing. Harvard's focus is to evaluate products to identify and eliminate the use of unnecessary chemical classes of concern and to show how code requirements can be met with natural alternatives.

Measuring Our Actions

When we act to reduce harmful chemicals in the built environment, does it actually make a difference? The Office of Sustainability worked with Dr. Anna Young, who created a research study in collaboration with Dr. Joe Allen and Dr. Elsie Sunderland, to answer this question (Young, 2022 and Harvard T.C. Chan School of Public Health, 2022). Dr. Young took dust samples in forty-six locations across campus before they were renovated. The refurbished spaces

Sunlight pours in through the many windows of the multi-tiered atrium in the Science and Engineering building in Allston at Harvard University. Rose Lincoln, Harvard Staff Photographer

were remodeled with carpet and furniture that specified the exclusion of PFAS and chemical flame retardants. The results confirm that when we act, we reduce harmful chemicals in our spaces: analyses of the samples revealed a 78 percent reduction in the sum of PFAS stain repellants and 65 percent reduction in the sum of certain chemical flame retardants.

HHBA Today

HHBA requirements are a foundation within Harvard's Sustainable Building Standards and currently include fourteen key interior product categories typically purchased by project teams. Harvard has leveraged its purchasing power to ask vendors and suppliers to transparently list all ingredients via health product declarations. This demand for transparency and optimization for health, especially when made by other large-scale purchasers, can positively influence the marketplace and optimize building materials for everyone, not just Harvard. These requirements have been achievable, too, as we identified healthier products that cost the same as their counterparts. As of 2023, Harvard has used HHBA Standards in more than fifty construction projects representing about 5 million square feet.

PFAS under Investigation

Synthetic PFAS chemicals have built up in our environment since they were first

Photo: Kris Snibbe, Harvard Staff Photographer

created in the 1930s. Exposure to these "forever chemicals" is associated with a range of health risks, such as cancer, immune suppression, diabetes, and low infant birth weight. PFAS can enter the air, water, and land, and has especially been studied in drinking water.

Earlier this year, Harvard scientist Elsie Sunderland, who serves as the Fred Kavli Professor of Environmental Chemistry and Professor of Earth and Planetary Sciences at the Harvard John A. Paulson School of Engineering and Applied Science (SEAS), and her research group published a paper on the dangers of PFAS-contaminated drinking water. Their research concluded that water contamination due to PFAS is significant in the vicinity of hundreds of U.S. military bases due to the use of aqueous film-forming foams for firefighting training and activities. And yet, these are not the only significant sources of PFAS entering and contaminating the drinking water: PFAS is also widely used as stain and water repellants in everyday products.

Much more research is needed to measure the total amount of PFAS in our drinking water, yet one thing our Harvard faculty can agree on is that we should stop using these forever chemicals where we can, including in the building materials for interior spaces.

HEALTHIER BUILDINGS; BETTER WORK PERFORMANCE

We know that people spend 90 percent of their time indoors, so indoor and outdoor air quality are both important to public health. There are many strategies to provide good indoor air quality, from air filtration and construction practices to healthier material selections and cleaning protocols.

Research conducted at the Harvard T.H. Chan School of Public Health (Carrier, 2023) by the Healthy Buildings Program is helping us quantify the benefits of improved IAQ. One study, led by Dr. Joseph Allen, used a real-life simulation tool to test the higher-order cognitive function of office workers at the standard-specified minimum air ventilation rate of 20 cfm/person compared to a higher rate of 40 cfm/person. When tested, participants' cognitive performance shifted upward from the 62nd to 70th percentile, compared to normative data of 70,000 people who had taken the cognitive tests in the past. This change in performance is equivalent to a $6,500 increase in salary per person per year. The energy costs of achieving the same change in ventilation totaled less than $40 per person per year, and dropped down to $1 per person per year when energy-efficient systems are used (Allen, 2017).

In addition to healthier materials selections, Harvard is piloting cost-effective and research-backed ventilation rate increases that balance health outcomes with leading energy performance.

IMPACT OUTSIDE OF HARVARD'S WALLS

Sharing our knowledge to drive solutions to global challenges is central to our mission. One example is our collaboration with the Massachusetts School Building Authority (MSBA), which is seeking to reduce harmful chemicals of concern in the state's public

SUSTAINABLY BUILT STRUCTURES AT HARVARD

Each new project allows us to expand our list of approved HHBA products and manufacturers, making it easier for project teams to meet the interior product category requirements. As more manufacturers provide healthier options, we have been able to achieve our goal of helping other organizations find, specify, and purchase healthier, affordable materials that are better for people and the planet.

Smith Campus Center
Harvard's Smith Campus Center renovation, completed in 2015, was Harvard's first Healthier Building Academy project. The project team specified the removal of at least three chemical classes of concern — PFAS, chemical flame retardants, and antimicrobials — in the carpet, furniture, flooring, and window treatments in the Smith Campus Center. With 3,000 pieces of furniture from twenty-seven furniture manufacturers (75 percent of whom had never made products that met our HHBA standards), it proved a perfect pilot project. In the end, all of the manufacturers met Harvard's standards on budget, and the job was completed on time. Furthermore, this highly-trafficked area has stood the test of time with beautiful, resilient materials that are easy to clean and maintain.

Science and Engineering Complex (SEC)
Harvard's Science and Engineering Complex (SEC), completed in 2021, was certified as one of the healthiest, most sustainable, and energy-efficient laboratories in the world. In addition to meeting our own HHBA standards for interior products, the 500,000-square-foot SEC achieved Living Building Challenge (LBC) Petal Certification for Materials, Beauty, and Equity, along with LEED Platinum certification.

During the construction of SEC, HHBA evaluated 6,000-plus building materials and collaborated with 1,200 companies, ultimately motivating many of them to publicly disclose the ingredients in their products and create transparency labels to help others make healthier decisions. The result led many manufacturing partners to reformulate

Photo: Kris Snibbe, Harvard Staff Photographer

their products to remove harmful classes of chemicals not just for Harvard, but for all customers. Such progress helps protect communities along the supply chain as well as people in the building.

The David Rubenstein Treehouse

Harvard is creating its first university-wide conference center, a state-of-the-art convening and innovation hub that will welcome visitors to the University's planned Enterprise Research Campus in Allston. This innovative project is designed by architecture and urban design firm Studio Gang, with sustainability consultant Perkins+Will, and built by Consigli-Smoot Construction.

Treehouse is targeting some of the highest sustainability standards addressing human and environmental well-being, including Living Building Challenge Core sustainable building certification. This building, including its commercial kitchen, will be all electric, and it will receive its power from Harvard's lower-carbon, climate-resilient District Energy Facility. The Treehouse roof will be used to harvest rainwater to be reused for irrigation and toilet flushing, and photovoltaics will provide emissions-free electricity.

As its name suggests, the building's design was informed by the branching structure of a tree and the experience of climbing into and inhabiting a treehouse. It is designed as a mass timber structure and, in combination with other lower embodied carbon materials, Treehouse is anticipated to reduce its embodied carbon by 50 percent compared to a conventional building. Also contributing to this reduction in embodied carbon are innovations such as using ground glass pozzolan replacements in concrete instead of traditional replacements like fly ash (a heavy metal-laden byproduct from burning coal). In addition, the project will meet HHBA requirements for all fourteen interior product categories.

The Greenway/Yard along the back of the new Science and Engineering Complex Building in Allston at Harvard University. Rose Lincoln, Harvard Staff Photographer

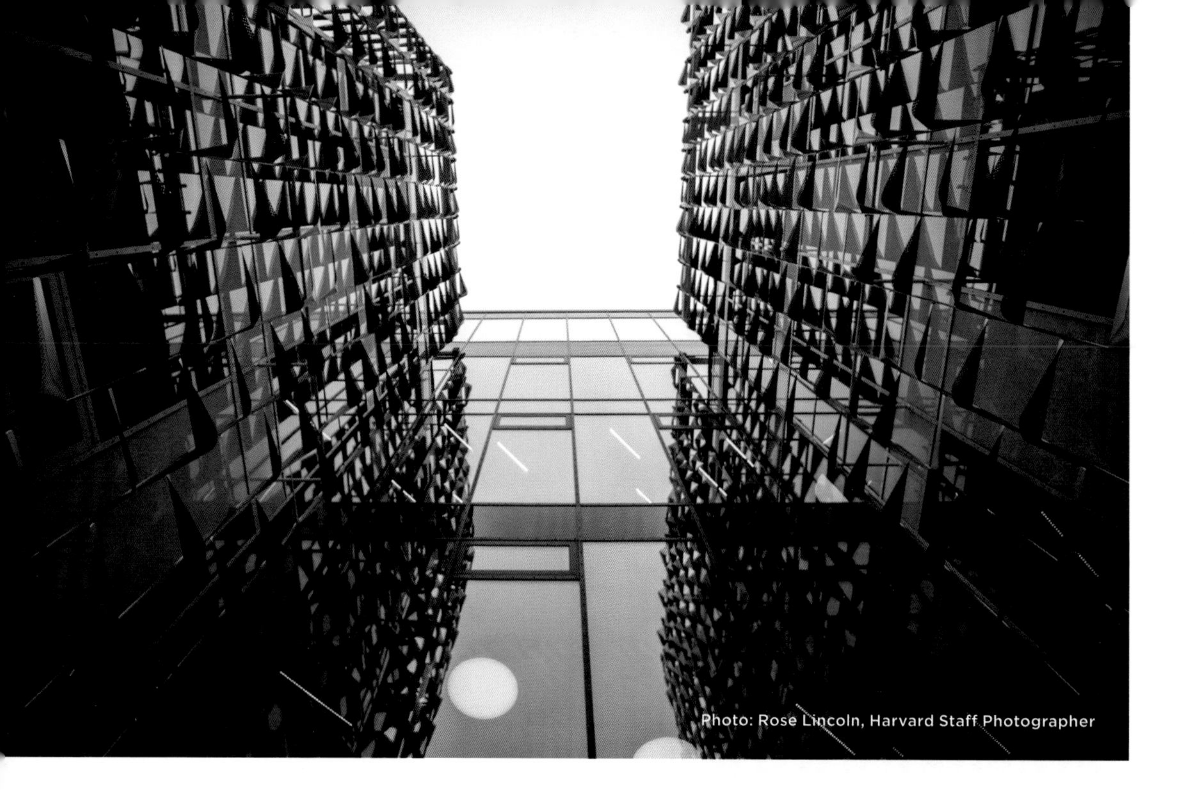
Photo: Rose Lincoln, Harvard Staff Photographer

schools. MSBA piloted these material health requirements in a new $305 million technical high school, marking the first time the MSBA has embarked on a project-wide initiative to reduce chemicals of concern that are linked to cancer, hormone disruption, and other health problems. The project required product transparency labels for health and used the HHBA playbook and research to help source healthier materials for their indoor spaces.

HHBA is encouraging more schools and large companies to leverage their buying power by first asking manufacturers for product transparency and then purchasing those optimized products that remove chemical classes of concern. We believe if there is sufficient market demand, we can drive manufacturers to remove chemicals of concern and greener chemistry will become the norm.

We are seeing results around this strategy as many large manufacturers evaluate their supply chains for chemicals of concern, phase them out where possible, and request greener, safer chemistry where alternatives do not exist. In addition to manufacturers, several states have existing or pending legislation directed at studying, reducing, or banning many chemicals of concern.

A HEALTHIER FUTURE

Harvard will continue to prioritize the Harvard Healthier Building Academy's mission to help transform the marketplace for healthier spaces and building products available for all. Ultimately, we want to help everyone make research and science-based decisions that holistically address climate, health, and equity in our built environment and supply chains so that we can all enjoy a healthy, thriving future.

Heather Henriksen has served as Harvard University's chief sustainability officer since 2008, advising the President and senior leadership on Harvard's university-wide sustainability strategy and policy. Heather leads the Office for Sustainability which ensures the University achieves its sustainability priorities and commitments including overseeing the comprehensive Sustainability Action Plan (co-created with faculty and students) and the University's Climate Action Plan (to be fossil fuel-free by 2050 and fossil fuel-neutral by 2026), which builds upon the 2016 achievement of Harvard's initial science-based climate goal.

REFERENCES

Allen, Joseph et al. (2017). ***The 9 Foundations of a Healthy Building***. Harvard T.H. Chan School of Public Health. forhealth.org/9_Foundations_of_a_Healthy_Building.February_2017.pdf

Carrier. (2023). ***The Impact of Green Buildings on Cognitive Function***. thecogfxstudy.com/

Harvard T.H. Chan School of Public Health. (2022, November 7). ***PFAS levels lower in buildings with healthier furnishings***. www.hsph.harvard.edu/news/press-releases/pfas-levels-lower-in-buildings-with-healthier-furnishings

President and Fellows of Harvard University. (2021). ***Recommendation from the Fossil Fuel Neutral by 2026 Subcommittee of the Harvard Presidential Committee on Sustainability***. sustainable.harvard.edu/wp-content/uploads/2023/05/Harvard-PCS-2026-Report.pdf

Young, A.S., Pickard, H.M., Sunderland, E.M., and Allen. J.G. (2022). Organic Fluorine as an Indicator of Per- and Polyfluoroalkyl Substances in Dust from Buildings with Healthier versus Conventional Materials. ***Environ. Sci. Technol***. 56, 23, 17090–17099. pubs.acs.org/doi/10.1021/acs.est.2c05198

THE OFFICE FOR SUSTAINABILITY (OFS) works across Harvard University to translate research and practice into action at the intersection of **climate, equity, and health** to show sustainable development at an institutional scale. Harvard's vision, priorities and goals for sustainability are detailed in our 2023 Sustainability Action Plan. OFS works with faculty, students, staff, alumni and external partners to accelerate the adoption of systems and practices that protect the climate and planet, advance a more equitable society, and promote the wellbeing of people at Harvard and beyond.

Sustainability at Harvard grew from a grassroot movement led by students and faculty which was formalized in 2008 by President Faust with the creation of the Office for Sustainability. Initially, OFS was charged with implementing a short-term climate goal to reduce absolute emissions at the University by 30% by 2016 while establishing a holistic sustainable development strategy. In 2014, Harvard released an inaugural Sustainability Action Plan. When the climate goal was met in 2016, even with institutional growth of 12%, Harvard set new goals to be fossil fuel-free by 2050, and fossil fuel-neutral by 2026.

OFS collaborates with Harvard stakeholders to achieve our goals and advance solutions to global system sustainable development challenges addressing climate, health and equity. OFS and Harvard also collaborate with state and federal partners as well as with community partners and the business sector to achieve shared sustainability goals.

The Red List: An Advocacy Tool for Market Transformation and Preventing Harm

Hannah Ray

The International Living Future Institute envisions a future where all materials in the built environment are regenerative and have no negative impact on human, community, and ecosystem health. In this ideal world, all ingredients within building products would be fully disclosed and free of toxicants and harmful chemicals.

However, there is no legal requirement for manufacturers of building materials to publish their ingredients. In addition, to reach this ideal vision, building material ingredients must also be screened, assessed, and optimized for health and environmental benefit.

ILFI's programs present a philosophy, advocacy tools, and certifications for projects to address this gap. In the area of material health, the Living Building Challenge (LBC) Red List serves as an advocacy tool for market transformation in the absence of regulation. Herein we describe the role of the Red List in spreading awareness and acting as a catalyst for change in encouraging the precautionary approach for chemicals of concern in buildings.

The Red List was conceived as a filter that enables practitioners to avoid specifying materials and products that contain harmful chemicals. Photo: Bernard Hermant/Unsplash

THE RED LIST

The LBC Red List is a list of chemicals representing the "worst in class" substances prevalent in the building industry that pose serious risks to human health and the environment. The Red List is organized by chemical class and lists individual chemicals by Chemical Abstract Registry Number (CASRN). Since its inception in 2006, the Red List has been an intuitive tool for communicating the need to stop using chemicals that cause harm.

The Red List is central to several of ILFI's programs, including the Materials Petal of LBC, the Living Product Challenge (LPC), and the Declare Label. Red List compounds must be avoided at the level of 100 ppm, or 0.01% of a product, in LBC projects, Red List Free Declare Labels, and LPC products and process chemicals. Temporary exceptions allowing selected Red List compounds in specific products exist within each program to reflect market realities. Overall, as a binary screen to assess material health, the Red List brings simplicity to a complex topic.

The chemical classes on the Red List range widely in structure, toxicity, and function. They include carcinogenic legacy building materials like lead in paint, asbestos, and polychlorinated biphenyls (PCBs) that are now illegal but still found in many existing buildings; chemicals that are regulated but not banned, like formaldehyde and other volatile organic compounds; and compounds of emerging concern that are pervasive in many products like ortho-phthalates, halogenated flame retardants, and per- and poly-fluoroalkyl substances (PFAS). The Red List also includes materials like polyvinyl chloride (PVC) that may not pose health risks in the finished product, but which have the potential for harm during the extraction, processing, manufacture, or disposal stages of the product life cycle. Red List compounds serve many different functions in many building products,

Short Term Health Effects of Chemical Exposure

Chronic Conditions Caused by Chemical Exposure

- Asthma
- Obesity
- Diabetes
- Heart Disease
- Neuro-Developmental Conditions
- Cancer

Photo: Bermix Studio/Unsplash

including drywall, insulation, adhesives, paint and other finishes, lighting fixtures, resilient flooring, waterproofing, textiles, and more. However, the use of these compounds can cause harm to health and the environment; hazards include cancer, reproductive toxicity, acute or chronic organ toxicity, endocrine disruption, persistence, ozone depletion, and others. Safer chemical alternatives, product designs, and building designs are possible: although prevalent, Red List compounds are not necessary in most instances.

The Red List is updated annually to stay current with science and policy. Early versions of the Red List flagged thirteen chemical classes and around 300 individual compounds. In 2023, the list comprised nineteen chemical classes and over 11,000 individual compounds. The Watch and Priority Lists, companion lists to the Red List, are updated quarterly.

The Watch List contains chemicals and compound groups under consideration for potential inclusion in the Red List. Designation as "Priority for Red List Inclusion" indicates ILFI's intent to add a given chemical to the enforceable Red List after spending at least twelve months on the Priority List.

POSITIVE IMPACTS

The Red List and ILFI's other programs such as Declare, LBC, and LPC, along with other programs like Enterprise Green Communities and LEED, have greatly raised awareness about the importance of material health within the regenerative building community. Diverse stakeholders reference or integrate the Red List in building standards, procurement policies, design strategies, and specifications. And thousands of manufacturers now voluntarily disclose ingredients and screen for the Red List.

CHEMICALS ON THE RED LIST CAN CAUSE THE FOLLOWING HEALTH AND ENVIRONMENTAL IMPACTS:

Health effects:

- Carcinogens, Mutagens, Reproductive hazards (CMR)
- Endocrine disruption
- Neurotoxicity, developmental toxicity, immunotoxicity
- Organ or system toxicity (acute or chronic)
- Asthmagens

Environmental impacts:

- Persistent, bioaccumulative, toxic (PBT)
- Very persistent and very bioaccumulative (vPvB)
- Persistent, mobile, and toxic (PMT)
- Very persistent and very mobile (vPvM)
- Ozone depletion
- Aquatic toxicity (acute or chronic)
- Antibiotic resistance

Each product or ingredient screened for an LBC project or a Declare label creates opportunities for education, advocacy, and positive change. Thanks to the regenerative building community's advocacy efforts, avoidance of Red List materials has sparked the innovation of new materials and design approaches that reduce the use of toxicants in buildings. For example, buildings can be designed with materials that do not require finishes, which often contain chemicals of concern, or without plenum spaces to maximize the use of low-smoke, halogen-free electrical cable. Formaldehyde-free insulation, PFAS-free carpet, and PVC-free shades are examples of products that have eliminated key chemicals of concern on the Red List.

Each product or ingredient screened for an LBC project or a Declare label creates opportunities for education, advocacy, and positive change. Thanks to the regenerative building community's advocacy efforts, avoidance of Red List materials has sparked the innovation of new materials and design approaches that reduce the use of toxicants in buildings.

At the time of this writing, the green building and material health community were aligning goals and strategies to work collectively toward making material optimization the norm rather than the exception.

FUTURE VISION FOR THE RED LIST

As our understanding of the health, environmental, and societal impacts of building materials increase in sophistication, the Red List and ILFI's other material health programs will need to evolve as well.

The true purpose of the Red List is to prevent harm — not to ban individual chemicals per se. To this end, ILFI is working on ways to strengthen the Red List and better articulate and achieve this goal. Revisions to our approach will be made in collaboration with our material health Technical Advisory Group and leading organizations working in this space. The revised approach may include specifying the harms to be prevented and publishing our methodology for updating the Red List in accordance with these goals. We are considering an evolution from a binary blanket ban to focus more on creating change in the greatest impact areas. Updated programs will also clearly place the achievement of being Red List Free as a first step (not the end goal) in the journey to full material health assessment and optimization. ILFI will provide positive guidance on selecting materials to safely use in buildings in addition to lists of what not to use.

Finally, as they evolve over time, ILFI's materials programs will further promote a holistic vision of what good looks like for materials, emphasizing green chemistry approaches to product development, regenerative rather than extractive feedstocks, innovative solutions to carbon sequestration and waste remediation, and attention to equity in supply chains and other life cycle stages.

Hannah L. Ray, Ph.D is the Senior Manager, Programs + Innovation (Materials), developing and managing the Declare program, the Living Product Challenge, the Materials Petal of the Living Building Challenge, and the Red List. She has professional experience managing R&D projects for an electrochromic glass manufacturer, and advocacy and material health research experience from the Green Science Policy Institute. Hannah received her Ph.D in Materials Science from U.C. Berkeley and her B.A. in Chemistry from Wesleyan University.

Photo: Arnaud Mesureur/Unsplash

PART III:

Climate + Environment

Think Supply Chain First: Supply Chains Are the Key to Social Equity, Human Health and Climate Goals

Kathleen Hetrick

With a new wave of consumer activism around the larger social impact of sustainable products and materials, it is no longer enough to claim a product to be low carbon, manufactured with 100 percent green energy, or utilizing recycled water. The raw materials and products we all rely on — the shoes on our feet, the insulation in our homes, the precious metals in our smartphones — must be sustainable from both an environmental and a social perspective.

Santa Monica City Hall East, designed by Frederick Fisher & Partners Architects, utilized a restrictive procurement process that excludes Red List chemicals. Photo: courtesy Amber Richane

The products of modern consumer culture — electronics, appliances, furniture, consumer care products, cars, clothing, packaging, and everything else in between — have complex and potentially damaging supply chains that affect people beyond direct consumers. Companies marketing sustainable products and services by today's standards don't always consider the true social impact at every level of their supply chains.

REEXAMINING EXTERNALITIES

When our teams at Buro Happold evaluate the true sustainability of any product, we include an accounting of the effects of materials and products on community health at every step in the product life cycle. This includes the miners, refinery workers and harvesters of raw materials used to make products, as well as factory workers, delivery workers bringing products to construction sites or to the customer's doorstep, and those responsible for disposing of or disassembling the product at the end of its use. We also consider not only the end user, but those who bear the heaviest burden of so-called externalities: communities living near power plants, production facilities, freight corridors, warehouse and port infrastructure, landfills, and construction sites.

Examples of environmental justice communities, where these industrial externalities are an everyday reality, are found in areas as diverse as Los Angeles, Philadelphia, Louisiana's "Cancer Alley," the Ohio River Valley, and hundreds of thousands of locations across the globe that lack the protections of activist oversight or well-established environmental law.

There is a common misconception that communities choose to live near polluting industries or land uses because these areas are more affordable, but that is simply not the case. Time after time, companies have shown a willingness to site polluting facilities (or unsightly elements of the supply chain, such as warehouses and waste-to-energy plants) where communities are disenfranchised or drowned out by industry lobbying.

In fact, many products, ranging from paint to insulation to commodity chemicals, are manufactured in clusters of facilities located around environmental justice communities as a way to cut costs, avoid negative press from more affluent communities, and to gain access to key material supply chains. The glaring inequities of industrial pollution raise urgent questions that sustainability experts across all industries continue to ignore. Rather than hidden in legal disclosures, social equity should instead be the guiding element in corporate social responsibility, materiality assessments, carbon accounting and sustainable building certification. Customer and investor demands for stronger, quantifiable ESG metrics and regenerative corporate strategy will reward the companies that act as catalysts for market-wide demand for transparency, decarbonization and toxic-free supply chains. Companies committed to either ignoring or contributing to environmental justice issues risk losing their social license to operate and falling out of step with new federal, state and international regulations.

The COVID-19 pandemic brought public health and related inequalities to the forefront of national news. The latest peer-reviewed research provides further evidence of the connection between increased COVID-19 mortality and exposure to hazardous air pollutants (HAPs) associated with manufacturing and nonrenewable resource consumption. Even beyond COVID-19, recent research and scientific studies highlight the various public health impacts of supply chains and material design. Executives, designers, and industry thought leaders must incorporate this extensive research into the corporate sustainability initiatives necessary for meeting their commitments to Environmental, Social and Corporate Governance (ESG) and climate action. It's a new approach, and a tough challenge, but luckily for companies all across the globe, regenerative change is possible if we commit to a triple bottom line approach, push for better alternatives to business as usual, and integrate human health and social equity into all supply chain and design decisions.

Figure 1. According to the National Institute of Health, approximately 80,000 new commercial synthetic chemicals have been released into the environment since World War II, with approximately 1500 new chemicals released annually.

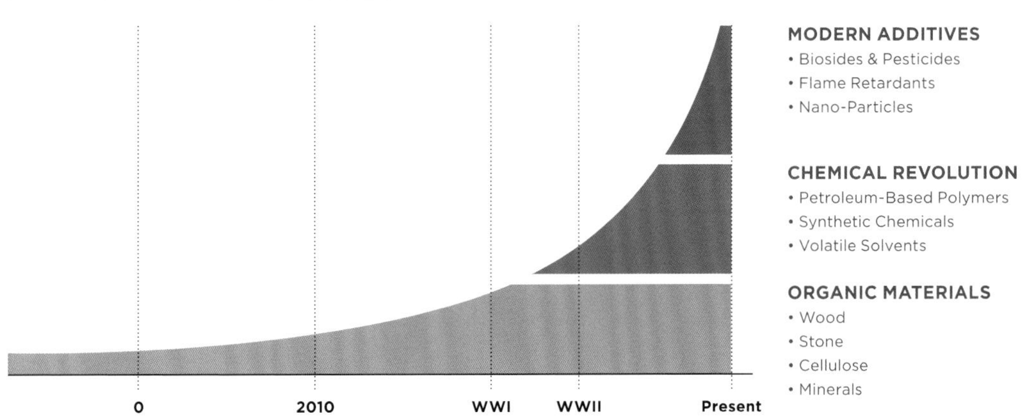

TURNING INDUSTRY INNOVATION INTO GREATER IMPACT

Transparency labels like Cradle to Cradle, Environmental Product Declarations, Health Product Declarations, Declare Labels, and the Living Product Challenge taken together with online product databases such as EC3, mindful MATERIALS, and Sustainable Minds form the essential social impact building blocks for procurement managers, designers, supply chain specialists, chemical engineers, and sustainability professionals alike. To unleash the potential of these tools, silos must be broken down and quantitative life cycle analysis and systems thinking incorporated into all elements of business, from flagship retail stores and the most profitable product lines to packaging.

We start by identifying the best-in-class examples for our relevant industry and related supply chain tiers, and then set the bar for our product development and procurement, identifying opportunities to overcome gaps in materials or local market constraints along the way. This requires using a multitude of tools to inform choices at a company or supply chain level, factoring in embodied carbon footprint, circularity, toxicity, and social impact. Integrating these tools and protocols into purchasing plans, development strategies, and design guidelines not only provides much-needed criteria and inspiration for improvements to products, but it also starts to form a culture where innovation leads to positive outcomes instead of future liabilities.

It is important to remember that despite green innovations and forward-thinking concepts like circularity, there are still hidden toxins, even in products that claim to be green. They are often hard to detect and can have unforeseen consequences when released into the environment — either during manufacture, by accident, or at the end of a building's or product's lifespan. Careful consideration of human and environmental health impacts must be taken across all stages of the life cycle, from cradle to cradle. The circularity movement goes hand in hand with designing for public health. By designing with the end in mind, those products — as well as buildings that aim for circularity — will also have to incorporate non-toxic design principles to allow for repurposing or reconfiguring.

As a complex, construction industry-level example, one of Buro Happold's Living Building Challenge (LBC) projects — Santa Monica City Hall East, designed by Frederick Fisher & Partners Architects — uses a restrictive procurement process that excludes all of the International Living Future Institute's Red List materials. The Red List represents the "worst in class" materials, chemicals, and elements known to pose serious risks to human health and the greater ecosystem that are prevalent in the building products industry. The World Health Organization (WHO), the Environmental Protection Agency (EPA) and the California Department of Public Health (CDPH) also publish details on Red List chemicals, which are available to the public. This "human health first" procurement strategy was applied to all of the building's products and materials, including steel, valves, carpet, and furniture, and led to solution improvements, game-changing conversations, and better outcomes for over 1,200 products that make up the building.

The journey to achieving Living Building Challenge certification for this 50,000-square-foot construction project opened our eyes to the fact that we cannot limit our standards for health and carbon impact to just building materials and their supply chains. If we care about human and environmental health, air quality, COVID-19, elevated cancer risk or any other number of public health crises, we must extend Red List-free criteria to our consumer care products, data centers, durables, food systems, and everything in between.

SUPPLY CHAINS FOR RISK REDUCTION & RESILIENCY

With climate change already in full force, we must also consider the possibility that building products might burn or be otherwise disturbed before the end of their planned life cycle, either intentionally during

Full Environmental Justice Accountability

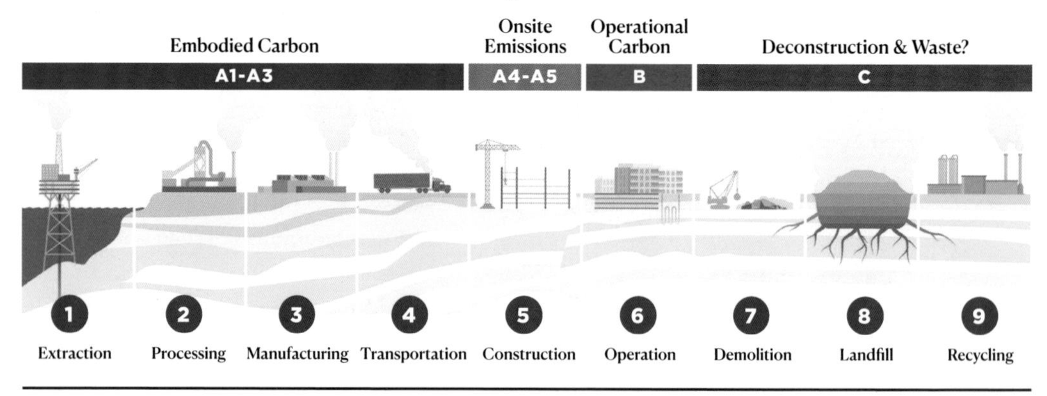

Figure 2. Creating truly regenerative buildings requires considering impacts to health, communiuties, and the environment at every step in the life cycle.

Santa Monica City Hall East.
Photo: courtesy Amber Richane

demolition or due to natural disasters such as earthquakes, floods, hurricanes, or wildfires. The risk of catastrophic events will only increase with continued delayed action on climate change, and community health impacts should be a key focus of any company's resiliency strategy. With new risks come new opportunities to protect public health and improve products. Removing the most problematic chemicals in supply chains — those that negatively impact environmental and human health at multiple life-cycle stages — will have outsized effects across multiple supply chains and assist the market in meeting the growing demand for safer, high-performing alternatives.

One such material of concern to consider phasing out is polyvinyl chloride (PVC). Recent news stories illustrate the connected impact of our inequitable material choices and the missed ESG strategies at every stage of the supply chain. For carcinogenic chemicals like polyvinyl chloride, the harm comes in many forms: from the climate change cost of cracking ethylene to the production and mining of the mercury, asbestos and PFAS needed for synthesis; from the occupational health hazards of vinyl chloride exposure to the train derailment in East Palestine, Ohio; from fake-wood flooring in our children's nurseries to labor issues half a world away.

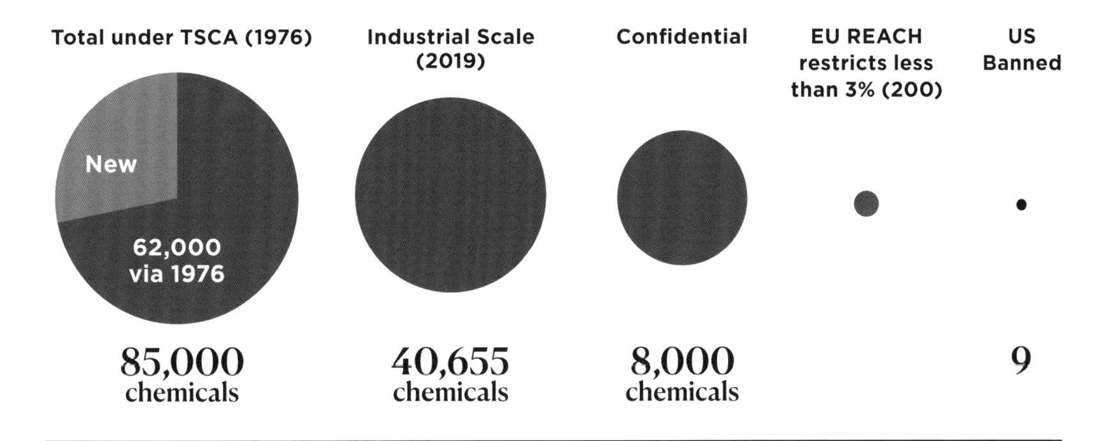

Figure 3. Of the 85,000 chemicals regulated under the federal Toxic Substance Control Act, only nine have been banned by the US EPA.

Widespread use of PVC in wiring, toys, consumer goods, medical equipment, flooring, and plumbing pipes can have detrimental health effects on consumers and building occupants. Their presence raises a new concern for those living in wildfire-prone regions. When burned, PVC has been found to emit hazardous substances such as dioxins, which are known carcinogens, into the air. Unsurprisingly, firefighters and other first responders, who are chronically exposed to burning chlorinated materials and other pollutants, suffer a 14 percent higher risk of dying from cancer than the general public. When plastic plumbing piping burns, it can leach harmful pollutants like benzene into drinking supplies, as happened in Santa Rosa, California, potentially compromising human health long after a fire is extinguished.

Starting the journey to replace a harmful material like PVC may be easy for some industries but transformational for others. Utilizing a restrictive list such as the ILFI Red List or REACH (a regulation of the European Union) may be new territory for many industries, but the innovation required to phase out harmful products will reduce risk and increase social license well into the future.

DESIGNING FOR THE FUTURE: REGENERATIVE DESIGN & SUPPLY CHAINS

Despite global climate commitments, fossil fuels play a key role in manufacturing many consumer and building products, even those touted as biophilic materials or healthy, natural products. Growth in demand for petrochemical products is on track to account for over a third of the total increase in oil demand to 2030, and nearly half to 2050. To decarbonize our economy and supply chains, fossil fuel-based plastics and petrochemicals must yield to sustainable alternatives wherever feasible.

With products relying on increasingly long, complex global supply chains, it can be difficult to determine if makeup, paint, children's clothing, or even essential medicines are petrochemical-based or reliant on petrochemical solvents at

Firefighters are exposed to a multitude of toxic chemicals in burning buildings and vehicles. Photo: Donomik Sostmann/Unsplash

Kathleen Hetrick is an Associate at Buro Happold and is a Bloomberg Fellow at the Bloomberg School of Public Health at Johns Hopkins University. As part of the Buro Happold Los Angeles Sustainability team, Kathleen combines her passion for regenerative design with a technical background in Architectural Engineering. She leads the sustainable design process on a wide range of cutting-edge projects, including LEED Platinum, ILFI Zero Carbon and Living Building Challenge buildings, portfolio-wide Scope 3 emissions reduction plans, social impact studies, resiliency analysis and corporate sustainability implementation workshops. She also facilitates Buro Happold's regional outreach initiatives to encourage local K-12 students to pursue sustainability-focused careers in STEM. She is currently a board member of USGBC-LA and is one of the founding instigators of Carbon Leadership Forum - Los Angeles. She is a recent recipient of the 2023 Living Future Hero Award.

BURO HAPPOLD

Buro Happold is an international, integrated consultancy of engineers, designers, and advisers, with a presence in thirty-five-plus locations worldwide, over eighty partners, and 2,500 employees. For over forty-five years we have built a world-class reputation for delivering creative, value-led solutions for an ever-challenging world.

burohappold.com

some stage. Levels of petrochemicals like benzene, toluene and other volatile organic compounds found in or emitted by end products might not be proven lethal to humans, but regulations across the world are becoming more stringent and are now examining health issues beyond acute toxicity to include chronic hormonal, carcinogenic, and neurological impacts that can occur at multiple levels of exposure. To meet organizational climate goals, sustainability teams must reconsider their products' reliance on commodity petrochemicals and determine if business as usual jeopardizes supply chain resilience, the health of our communities, the future of our planet, or brand loyalty and reputation.

Sustainability leaders within companies have many different ways to promote transformational change: as consumers, decision makers, product developers and specifiers. At Buro Happold, we can help companies design products, reimagine supply chains, develop procurement guidelines, refine operations, and engineer buildings to zero energy and waste standards, while minimizing synthetics that are harmful to humans and biodiversity. From cradle to cradle, the products and services companies deliver should not harm human health; instead, they should do regenerative good and help mitigate climate change whenever possible. We are aggressively working toward this goal at Buro Happold, and we are excited to support anyone with a similar vision.

Through innovative projects and better practices, we can transform the materials marketplace for zero-carbon and Red List-free alternatives that benefit all of society. The time has come for sustainability leaders to show the rest of the world how to design our buildings and products to have a positive impact on the environment and human health.

Believe in Better through Emergent Thinking: Blueprint for the Future

Malisa Maynard

Myriad challenges — the well-being of workers, the health of ecosystems and communities, loss of biodiversity — are expanding and complicating how we approach climate change. For these reasons, it is an extraordinary and pivotal time to be part of global manufacturing.

The Social Canvas carpet tile collection grew out of Mohawk's partnership with ArtLifting to support marginalized artists.

Manufacturers face many of the same challenges around the world, from water scarcity and energy use to questions about carbon and equity. Where Mohawk seeks to be unique is through our actions and our leadership in the transition to what's next. We have looked deeply, and often uncomfortably, at past, present, and future actions, and developed our belief in our inherent responsibility: to not only be responsive to these challenges but to anticipate them, to change them, and to reshape our thought processes and reframe our expectations around process, profit, and impact.

We at Mohawk Industries clearly understand that the actions we take today will determine the future. And we will make that a resilient future if we commit to a regenerative mindset and develop and execute innovative processes that actualize our ambitions.

REGENERATIVE APPROACH

A sense of environmental stewardship was in place long before I joined Mohawk Industries, and even before I understood the current definition of sustainability. It was something organic and intrinsic, linked to the images from some of my earliest memories.

I grew up in the Rocky Mountains of Montana, and I have a deep appreciation for the beauty of the outdoors and time spent, in companionship or in solitude, enjoying the region's rivers, mountains, forests, wildflowers, and wildlife set against the backdrop of the big, open skies for which Montana is known.

I was lucky to spend time with four generations of my family. This multigenerational history instilled in me not only a love of family but also an understanding that many of their sacrifices were made to build a better future for their children and grandchildren, in ways that made deep and natural sense to them. My Great-Grandma Violet's house was built on the banks of the Bitterroot River. She grew up during the Great Depression, and her focus on conservation and reuse was very much a result of a strongly ingrained survival mindset and time-tested resilience that she learned from her parents. My Grandpa Phil spent his days in the forest working for the logging industry; he appreciated and respected nature and was proud of being able to provide timber for families to build homes. My dad followed in his father's footsteps, working at a sawmill for more than fifty years with this same respect and appreciation.

Living in the country with more animals than people, my brother and sister were my best friends. On outings to town, people would notice my two siblings in wheelchairs. I remember thinking that I just wanted everyone to see them for the amazing people that I knew and not focus on their disabilities. Through them I learned that

every person could contribute to society in a unique way, and that inclusion can be a unifier as well as a catalyst for change.

I have spent my career in manufacturing, and many of the places where I have worked are small, rural towns where industry plays an integral part in generating income and support for the community. With a narrow view, one might assume that my life and my career are in conflict with the contemporary concept of sustainability. For me, it is the heart of the work — to understand what needs to be done to protect the planet and our future while keeping our people employed and our economy strong, all while manufacturing products that we use every day. By taking care of what you have, reserving judgment, seeking out and implementing new perspectives, there is no challenge for which you cannot find a solution.

When I look back over my career, I see twenty-five years of improvements in sustainability made by hard-working people who chose to do the right thing. Like my grandparents, like my communities, like me, they all believed in employing regenerative approaches to make things better.

JOURNEY TO NET POSITIVE PRODUCTS

Mohawk's roots can be traced back to the late 1800s as a small carpet and rug manufacturer. Principles of sustainability have informed the company's mindset and culture since the beginning. Even the company name reflects the importance of natural resources in the company's early years: the Mohawk River winds

through Amsterdam, New York, where the organization established its first manufacturing plant. Today, Mohawk has grown into the world's largest, most comprehensive flooring manufacturer. Its size gives the company the unique ability to practice sustainability on a large scale for an even greater impact, and it also bestows an equal scale of responsibility. Coupled with the magnitude of our sustainability challenges — the health, equity, and climate crises we currently face — we have never been more committed or better prepared to lead the transition to a more sustainable, inclusive, climate-positive economy.

When I joined Mohawk in 2021, I immediately observed the sustainability focus on conservation and efficiency within the business. During my first week on the job, I discovered an archived *Mohawk Repair Job Ticket* from 1947 titled "Use Less! Waste Less!" This spoke to me.

This resource conservation philosophy is still pervasive, three-quarters of a century later. Every business unit within the company prioritizes innovation as a means for improving and simplifying its processes. The approach is entrepreneurial, and the success of the company is personal for each employee.

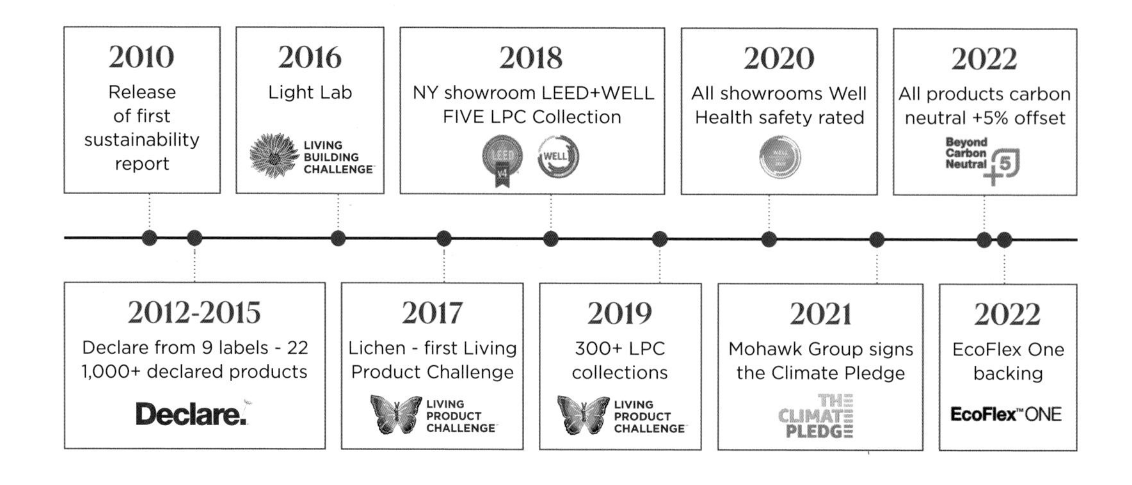

Figure 1. This timeline marks some of the major milestones of Mohawk's sustainability journey.

What can be tricky about moving the needle in an organization already committed to sustainability and regenerative practices is the breadth of that commitment itself. There is always so much work to do, so many new avenues to explore, so much urgency to execute and pivot to every new sustainability trend. The challenge, then, is in prioritization.

For guidance, we look to the pillars of Mohawk's sustainability strategy: People, Planet and Performance. These pillars are fundamentally interconnected and interdependent, helping us align, gain clarity, and purposefully direct our actions.

"At Mohawk we're proud to be at the forefront of flooring sustainability - in our products and our processes, as well as in how we think about people and community, and our responsibilities in those areas," says Paul De Cock, Mohawk's president of Flooring North America. "One of our guiding principles is Reinvestment in People and the Planet, and we are continuously evaluating how we can apply that through innovation, design and every other aspect of our work, every day."

With manufacturing operations in nineteen countries and thousands of products, it's challenging to catalog all of Mohawk's efforts in sustainability; however, we can highlight a few ways we have set clear, focused priorities aligned to these pillars, regenerative thinking and the concept of "believing in better" on our journey to net-positive products.

Each business within Mohawk has an individual sustainability journey; we learn from one another to accelerate our collaborative actions. Within our Flooring North America business, Mohawk Group serves our commercial customers. Mohawk Group's sustainability journey demonstrates how the overall strategies that are driving our sustainability initiatives play out through actions within each business.

DATA TIDE: WATER AND BIOPHILIA IN DESIGN

Data Tide is an innovative carpet tile system created by Mohawk Group. Data Tide explores the symbiotic relationship between nature and data through visual landscapes. The aim is to highlight biodiversity and water's essential role for survival in the natural world. The Mohawk Group design team used data sets from scientific studies of blue carbon to express biophilic patterns through data visualization, while humanizing the data to create a visual translation of water from information to product.

"Blue carbon" refers to the carbon dioxide sequestered by plants in coastal estuaries. The convergence of freshwater with saltwater in these estuaries creates unique ecosystems; here, salt marsh plants, mangroves and seagrass sequester blue carbon and protect coastal areas from sea-level rise and storm surges. It is imperative to protect river ecosystems from habitat destruction to maintain these ecosystems.

Research led the Mohawk Group design team to studies from Duke University's Nicholas Institute for Environmental Policy Solutions and the *Guidance on National Greenhouse Gas Inventories* from the United States Intergovernmental Panel on Climate Change. The team learned that more carbon is captured underwater than on land by trees and plants (biomass), and this is the data that inspired the pattern work.

Mohawk's Living Site in Glasgow, Virginia, produces over 300 certified Living Product carpet tile products.

Data Tide was designed to be biomimetic: the patterns and colors feature a gradient that imitates how light reflects off river waves. The palette is also authentic to estuaries, where rivers meet the ocean. The carpet collection is comprised of three styles of 12" x 36" planks: Aqua Rhythm is an active pattern, River Code is a textural pattern, and Biome is a tonal loop texture, referencing different ecosystems such as forest, ocean, and grassland. All styles share the same gradating colorways that range from dark to light, just like transitions of light to dark tones in bodies of water. The color palette was also influenced by the natural elements of estuaries, deltas, and marshes. Reflecting the merging of river and ocean, a new visual was created with the confluence of textures. The fibers used in Data Tide are a unique combination of solid yarns, heathered yarns and twisted yarns which together create rich, dimensional textures that celebrate the movement of water.

"Flooring has a big role to play on a building project because it supports the quality of life of end-users and communities," says Royce Epstein, Mohawk Group's A&D Design Director. "A carpet product like Data Tide addresses every aspect: performance, aesthetics, materiality, sustainability, emotional well-being, health and transparency, equity, and even aspirational qualities such as feeling grounded and safe." Data Tide is made at Mohawk's Living Site in Glasgow, Virginia, a historic manufacturing plant sited between two rivers. Data Tide has achieved Petal certification from the

Data Tide is beyond carbon neutral and Net Positive Water, with offsets exceeding 5 percent beyond neutral. These offsets come from global carbon equity projects and water conservation initiatives supporting Blue Carbon.

International Living Future Institute's Living Product Challenge, is Red List Free of chemicals of concern, and is also net positive for both carbon and water. Data Tide is beyond carbon neutral and Net Positive Water, with offsets exceeding 5 percent beyond neutral. These offsets come from global carbon equity projects and water conservation initiatives supporting Blue Carbon.

As part of Mohawk Group's handprint initiatives with the Living Product Challenge, a portion of the proceeds from the sale of this collection benefits water-related conservation organizations, such as Waterkeeper Alliance and Change the Course.

"Mohawk Group recognizes that water plays a vital role in ecology and biodiversity, but also has economic and social impacts around the globe," says Mike Gallman, Mohawk Group's president.

HANDPRINTS AND SOCIAL CO-BENEFITS: GIVING BACK MORE THAN WE TAKE

Mohawk Group began work with the ILFI in 2012 by exploring Declare label certifications. Building off that work, Mohawk Group developed its first Living Product Challenge certification in 2017, with the Lichen collection. In 2019, Mohawk Group achieved Living Product Challenge certification for its entire commercial nylon carpet tile collection made at the company's Living Site in Glasgow, Virginia. Because certification had expanded to cover more collections, Mohawk Group had a larger water footprint to balance than ever before, which presented a great

In 2019, Mohawk Group achieved Living Product Challenge certification for its entire commercial nylon carpet tile collection made at the company's Living Site in Glasgow, Virginia. Because certification had expanded to cover more collections, Mohawk Group had a larger water footprint to balance than ever before, which presented a great opportunity to integrate social co-benefits.

opportunity to integrate social co-benefits. That year, Mohawk Group partnered with historically Black colleges and universities such as Morehouse College, Benedict College, Hampton University and Alabama State University to retrofit dorms with low-flow, high-efficiency showerheads. The showerheads not only save millions of gallons of water annually, but also allow the institutions to use the money saved to fund scholarships and programs to educate students on regenerative sustainability. For Mohawk Group's 2022 recertification period of the Social Co-benefits imperative, the company once again integrated social co-benefits into our Water Handprint strategy. In addition to the Water Restoration Credit efforts referenced above, Mohawk Group connected with Water.org through its partnership with The Climate Pledge. Mohawk Group developed this partnership to further work on projects that both reduce water consumption and provide clean water access in developing countries. These options provide excellent opportunities to give back more water than is consumed and ease the strain of water insecurity in places of need. The Social Co-benefits imperative is one of the many reasons Mohawk Group chose and continues to certify products with the Living Product Challenge over other multi-attribute certifications available in the market. ILFI offers the best programs to communicate Mohawk Group's Better for People values in addition to the Better for the Planet and Better Performance values. By offering the Social Co-benefits Imperative, the Living Product Challenge offers truly holistic sustainability certification for Mohawk Group's products.

SAVING WATER WITH COLOR PULSE™

The tonal look, a dispersion of multiple colors or color values across the length of the yarn, is a popular styling technique used to achieve multi-color looks and textures in carpet. In the past, this effect could only be achieved through a process known as space-dyeing, which requires water both for the application of the colorants and for washing away unfixed dyes. The significant amounts of water used in the space-dying process must then go through additional purification processes before being released, resulting in additional energy and emissions.

To deliver an alternative to space-dyeing that reduced water use, Mohawk Group developed a proprietary, patent-pending technology called Color Pulse that provides the same tonal effect to the carpet fibers but without the use of water.

"Color Pulse is a tremendous step forward in reducing natural resource consumption without compromising the desired design," says Carlos Carrillo, VP of Research and Development at Mohawk. "This patent pending extrusion technology creates a fiber with selective reflectance to highlight colors, yielding a tonal effect in yarns."

This new process saves up to one cup of water per carpet tile compared to traditional space-dyed yarns and is part of the company's comprehensive strategy to reduce water consumption.

PROVIDING A PLATFORM FOR ARTISTS

While Data Tide was inspired by Mohawk Group's commitment to conserving and protecting water resources, the company's Painted Perspectives and Social Canvas collections reflect our commitment to equity, diversity, and social impact. These collections were launched in 2022 through a partnership with ArtLifting, a benefit corporation which provides artists with disabilities as well as those who have experienced housing insecurity with a platform for their artwork to be recognized and celebrated. This partnership epitomizes the Better for People philosophy and goes beyond traditional sustainability, which focuses on environmental impacts.

"We believe that visibility is a key component of designing for equity, diversity and social impact," says Jackie Dettmar, vice president of Marketing, Design and Product Development at Mohawk Group. "We are making our values visible through the inclusion of visual artists who are often excluded from the mainstream art world. These collaborative projects allow talented individuals to explore new modes of expression, introduce them to new audiences and expand their sphere of opportunity... and create beautiful and lasting products for commercial spaces."

BETTER TOGETHER

The sustainability milestones on Mohawk's journey to net-positive products and a regenerative future have measurable impacts that demonstrate a focus on design-forward thinking, product innovations and social co-benefits, all creating change in the built environment and beyond. To deliver these innovations, Mohawk has had to balance short-term cost with long-term investment, as well as address and reframe the industry status quo. In general, for companies to invest in and implement sustainability programs, genuine behavior and mindset changes are required, which sometimes can take years to fully realize. However, an integrated approach that respects the past while prioritizing the future is key for ensuring that every company, team, and individual has an important role in overcoming industry challenges.

Personally, I believe it comes down to one word: better. It's something to strive for, something to demand, something to believe in. Better is something everyone can strive for at the individual level, on a ranch in Montana or at the highest seat in a Fortune 500 company. Every positive action matters and everyone can achieve better — but no individual, business, industry or sector can solve all of today's challenges.

A regenerative, equitable and inclusive, climate-positive economy depends on all people to drive change. Let's work to create a regenerative future and invest in materials, products and processes that are better.

Malisa Maynard is Chief Sustainability Officer for Mohawk Industries and leads the company's environmental, social, and governance (ESG) strategy to enhance and strengthen Mohawk's overall performance. With more than 20 years of experience in sustainability within several manufacturing industries, Maynard is passionate about proactive ESG engagement and believes long-term, measurable success depends on acting now. Before serving in corporate sustainability leadership roles, Maynard used her skills as an environmental engineer to optimize sustainability within manufacturing operations. Maynard grew up on a ranch in Montana, where she developed a deep appreciation for nature. She believes we must work together as a community of stakeholders to ensure the security and prosperity of future generations.

Embodied Carbon: Now the Hard Work Begins

Donald W. Davies

It's fair to say that action for reducing embodied carbon within the built environment has pivoted from peripheral chatter to a front-and-center topic. It's even reached our nation's capital with the enactment in August 2022 of the $369-billion Inflation Reduction Act — often referred to as the "climate bill" because it funds a host of climate-related initiatives, including a $250-million investment in a national program for Environmental Product Declarations (EPDs). These actions are game-changing advancements from where the conversation was just a short time ago.

The momentum is wonderful, and we should be pleased with the success. But what happens next?

Reducing the embodied carbon of new buildings is one of our greatest opportunities — and one of our greatest challenges. Photo: Fons Heijnsbroek/Unsplash

When creating the built environment, we talk about what is possible. But we also often stop short of taking the steps needed to realize many of those possibilities. Changing how our industry operates, especially related to embodied carbon, is no easy task. It requires vision, in-the-weeds detail work, and the determination to play the long game. As we move toward a more climate-conscious future, we must act and address several notable challenges and opportunities.

CHALLENGE NO. 1 — MOVING THE BASE

Floods. Forest fires. Heat waves. Droughts. Hurricanes. Mother Nature is delivering messages that we need to build in ways that slow down the pace of global warming. But even in the face of these warnings, many people within the building industry will not act or make a meaningful change until two things happen: climate change personally affects them in a negative way, or change makes financial sense to their business. Consider Life Cycle Analysis (LCA) — a data-driven process that measures, estimates, and speculates on a project's various environmental factors, including embodied carbon. LCA allows our industry to make more informed and mindful decisions about a project's lifespan, systems, materials, and the suppliers from which we source. For example, concrete's LCA reveals that a project's cement quantities comprise much of its up-front carbon impacts. But cement is essential to concrete's strength, durability, and speed of construction. Using too little cement can reduce longevity, especially in weather-exposed locations and foundations. It also often leads to inconsistent concrete mixes and slower construction. LCA helps us compare the carbon footprint of the alternatives — *What are the lifetime carbon impacts of choosing certain types of concrete? What are the comparative values of lower carbon cement or cement replacements? Does a lower carbon alternative to concrete exist?* — and make more informed decisions about how and where we act on what we find. Indeed, LCA is a powerful measuring and reporting tool that is key to reducing our built environment's global warming impacts. And yet, many people in our industry see LCAs as complicated, burdensome, and financially not in their interest. So we must still work to prove its value, understanding that most people will act and make changes when it serves their financial interests, not when they have been converted to a different way of thinking.

That is our benchmark for this challenge — making the financial benefits of doing LCAs real. We need to create more incentives that encourage our industry to adopt LCA as the carbon measurement and reduction management process around which we organize.

Photo: Matt Palmer/Unsplash

Photo: anatoliy_gleb/iStock

CHALLENGE NO. 2 — PRACTICING WHAT WE PREACH

We also need to do a better job following through when making commitments. For example, the AIA 2030 Commitment — an actionable climate strategy launched in 2010 aiming for net zero emissions in the built environment — drew the interest of more than 1,120 signatory firms dedicated to the cause. But unfortunately, only a small fraction of these firms have reported their annual data since the program started, according to DesignIntelligence's (DI) report entitled *Refresh Refocus Reenergize*. Further from that DI industry survey, more than 600 firms failed to report *any* data; among the 410 firms that submitted *some* data, only 271 provided more than 60 percent of the data requested.

The initial work of Architecture 2030 and the AIA 2030 Commitment provided much-needed early leadership. But for meaningful change, we need to now move beyond well-intentioned commitments with aspirational goals. We also need to consistently collect and share comparable and strategically anonymized data within industry databases that allow us to track our progress better. This will happen when our clients make commitments and seek out design professionals and contractors who can best help them reach those commitments. In doing so, they hold themselves and those working for them accountable. When LCA leadership and expertise decide who gets the work, and there are incentives for the results achieved, then this change becomes real.

These industry advancements might seem like a sea change, but they are already happening. In April 2022, the international developer Hines became a leader in the lower embodied carbon space by releasing its *Embodied Carbon Reduction Guide* — a free, publicly available document providing a transparent roadmap for how Hines is changing its decision-making processes to include LCA as a core part of its work. In addition, Hines is re-writing its RFPs for consultants and contractors, requiring both knowledge of and deliverables around LCA decision-making.

Hines isn't the only progressive developer to adopt LCA and reap the benefits of reductions in cost, carbon, and risk. When quantities and embodied carbon are estimated and tracked during early project stages and then carefully managed through the full design and construction process, best practice project management is brought forward. While Hines and other smart developers are picking up on this added risk reduction benefit, many others are deterred, assuming that added work will only lead to added costs.

To make progress on this challenge, we need to remove perceived and real barriers that prevent our clients from using LCA as a decision-making tool. That includes education up and down the development, design, and construction food chain, as well as easily accessible LCA tools that use the same LCA datasets and that align with how to work with the available data. It also requires us to practice what we preach by consistently sharing case studies and common database information in a way that advances our understanding of the carbon footprints of what and how we build. By aligning our data reporting and following through, we will enable better embodied carbon metrics, which will help our clients tell more credible comparative stories and further incentivize lower carbon projects.

OPPORTUNITY: WHERE WILL THE NEXT INCENTIVES TO CHANGE COME FROM?

Financial institutions and the federal government. Measuring, comparing, and optimizing the decision-making around our built environment's carbon footprint is growing in new places. The banking and finance industries are starting to focus on environmental, social, and governance factors when considering where to invest. The United States Securities and Exchange Commission has begun enacting rules around accountability and forecast modeling that require climate impacts to be considered and reported. The United States federal government is starting to invest billions of dollars in low-interest loans and grants with carbon-accounting strings attached.

When these organizations — and the agents, accountants, oversight boards, and legal parties to which they report — place value on credible carbon data as part of their financial reporting and disclosures, our industry is sure to change.

Increasingly, aspirational goals will not be enough for our clients to secure funding from government, banking, and financial institutions. They will need to show measurable proof of lower embodied carbon in their projects. In turn, the incentive to change will pivot from voluntary to required. Developers, designers, and contractors who anticipate this forthcoming change and adjust their business practices in advance will find a competitive advantage.

FOUR NEXT LCA STEPS

While industry momentum is building, we must improve our LCA processes to keep this momentum from spiraling in unproductive directions. Here are four steps we need to take to advance LCA and bolster its credibility:

1. Agree on a Common Carbon Baseline. We need to make it easier to compare projects. Measuring from "zero" is probably the easiest to explain to others. But so many questions remain. What is the timeframe? Upon what data is it based? Should we only track and report the upfront carbon required to build? Should we measure to a consistent 60- or 100-year timeframe? Should we only measure the structure? Should we include the site impacts and temporary works consumed? What about the finishes and contents over time? We sorely need alignment on what to measure, when to measure, and how to compare. CLF, ILFI, USGBC, BREEM, Architecture2030 and others are doing good work here, but these questions do not yet have consistent answers that industry follows.

2. Establish Comparable Data Between Materials and Projects. The reporting inconsistencies within materials and project types are wide and often contentious. Until inter-material reporting compatibility, data transparency, and project measuring are better aligned, we should *at least* include the range of possible outcomes within the numbers we *do* report — especially when findings are directionally informative but inconclusive.

3. Estimate, Measure, and Report Material Quantities throughout Design and Construction. We talk about this today, but within the North American design and construction practices, few consistently provide this information in a way that allows for LCA modeling without significant speculation.

4. LCA for Actionable Decision Making and Project Accountability. LCA should not be a one-time snapshot. It should start with a project-specific baseline, include progress checks and actionable data comparisons, and end with final as-built reporting that is compared to early project goals, as well as being anonymized and submitted to an industry-wide database. Along the way, the data considered, the questions asked, and the findings reported will evolve.

These are not difficult concepts, but they require industry-wide coordination and action that have yet to happen consistently and collectively.

WHEN "BUSINESS AS USUAL" CHANGES

Global warming and its impact on the planet is a front-and-center topic. Our use of LCA to measure and then manage and optimize embodied carbon in our projects is certainly part of our call to action.

We are seeing progress, and with developers, their lenders, and the federal government all focusing on what it takes to lower the embodied carbon of what we build, the pace of change is only increasing. But to fully bring LCA into our decision-making, we need to move the industry base in new ways. It's not enough to

Of the three materials considered for construction of the PAE Living Building Headquarters in Portland, Oregon, wood reduces embodied carbon by approximately 25 percent compared to concrete or steel frames. With wood holding up the structure, the project's remaining concrete (primarily found in the building's core, foundation, and topping slab) accounts for about one-third of the building's embodied carbon. Photo: Lara Swimmer, courtesy PAE Engineers

wait for someone else to act first before getting involved. Consider engaging with your local chapter of the Carbon Leadership Forum's Embodied Carbon Action Network or learn about Building Transparency and its free and open-access tools. Connect with your relevant practice area of AIA2030, SE2050, or MEP2040. Get involved in Architecture2030, the International Living Future Institute, and the U.S. Green Building Council.

With this approach, you will begin to better understand how to navigate the contentious and sometimes uncomfortable spaces around embodied carbon. You will find that, while everyone may not agree, finding alignment for collective action is possible. Be it from developer requirements, the SEC, or the Buy Clean policy discussions happening at all levels of government today, the opportunities to influence the language that will drive this alignment are many. These rules and policies are shaped by those who choose to get involved, so don't wait for others.

What now? You and your peers — designers, owners, advocates, and manufacturers involved in the architecture, engineering and construction industry — leaning in collectively on these challenges, opportunities, and next steps will transform "business as usual" to a new, more sustainable status quo.

Don Davies, PE, SE is Co-Founder and Principal with Davies-Crooks Associates and Board Chair for Building Transparency. Don is an industry champion for the promotion of urban density and low-carbon construction. He helped found the Carbon Leadership Forum, Building Transparency, and the MKA Foundation. Don has led the collaborative teams that developed both the Hines Embodied Carbon Reduction Guide, and the MKA Low Carbon Concrete Procurement Guide.

The past president of Magnusson Klemencic Associates, his structurally designed projects are in 18 countries and more than 50 major metropolitan centers. More than 25 are Performance Based Seismic Designed towers. Don is a Senior Fellow of the Design Futures Council, and he has been inducted into the UC Berkeley Academy of Distinguished Alumni.

Our Biophilic Response to Wood

William Browning

Humans have an innate affinity for nature — a phenomenon known as biophilia (Wilson, 1984).

This connection has become the subject of many research initiatives exploring how different experiences of nature affect humans both physiologically and psychologically, leading to the recognition that designing elements of nature into the built environment can have health benefits. These benefits, which include stress reduction, improved cognitive performance, enhanced moods, and increased preference for spaces (Ryan, 2014), are often referred to as "biophilic responses."

The use of wood in the spaces and places where we live, work and play definitively supports a biophilic response. There is evidence that the presence of wood surfaces in a space can have a number of psychological and physiological benefits. Wood is often described as being "warm, comfortable, relaxing, natural and inviting," and people believe that "wood can help to

The choice of wood for the structure of the PDX Terminal Redevelopment in Portland, Oregon, had three main drivers: a desire to celebrate local nature, history, culture and business; to improve the embodied carbon and sustainability profile for the building; and to optimize the impact of the biophilic experience for occupants. Rendering: courtesy Port of Portland and ZGF Architects

create healthful environments" (Rice, 2006). There is some experimental work that has investigated biophilic responses to wood, much of which is focused on response to wood as a visual element within an interior space. The visual presence of wood in a room can lead to perceptions of warmth (Blackenberger, 2019). In a room with white walls, the addition of wood surfaces has shown to lower stress more effectively than the addition of a few plants (Fell, 2015). In other research, rooms with about 45 percent of the surfaces being wood have shown to boost perceptions of comfort and lower blood pressure (Herz, 2004), even among study participants who expressed a dislike for the wood (Sakuragawa, 2005).

Our love for wood is likely partially through association with life, partially through scent and touch, a bit through color, and largely due to the inherent patterns of wood grain. The array of biophilic responses to wood present clear topics that warrant more investigation to understand the underlying causality.

In the design of Common Ground High School in New Haven, Connecticut, Gray Organschi Architecture used a variety of wood construction techniques. A comment by the students is that they like the smell of the wood in the building. Photo: David Sundberg/ESTO Photographics

OLFACTORY RESPONSE

There is some evidence that certain compounds found in the scent of some woods, like linalool (Harada, 2018) and limonene (Grote, 2021), trigger positive physiological and psychological responses. Some forest bathing research also points in this direction, although the number of participants in the studies is too limited to allow good statistical analysis (Ikei, 2015). While there is some evidence for olfactory response, in many cases there is no perceptible scent to wood in a space.

HAPTIC (TOUCH) RESPONSE

Increased activity of the parasympathetic (rest and calming) portion of the nervous system has been tied to the experience of touching an oak panel, but not stainless steel, tile, or marble (Ikei, 2017). Haptic experiences of wood are evidenced to also lower systolic blood pressure (Morikawa, 1998) (Sakuragawa, 2008). These results may be due to wood having lower thermal conductance than metal or stone, thus feeling closer to the perceived ambient temperature of a space. The heightened parasympathetic activity and lowered blood pressure may be due to thermal conductance, or to the tactile feel (perception of touch) of wood surfaces, or perhaps both.

The entry at Vancouver Island University features Douglas Fir slabs and door pulls. The texture of the wood is the first thing people feel when they engage with the building. Photo: Barker Manufacturing Inc., courtesy naturallywood.com

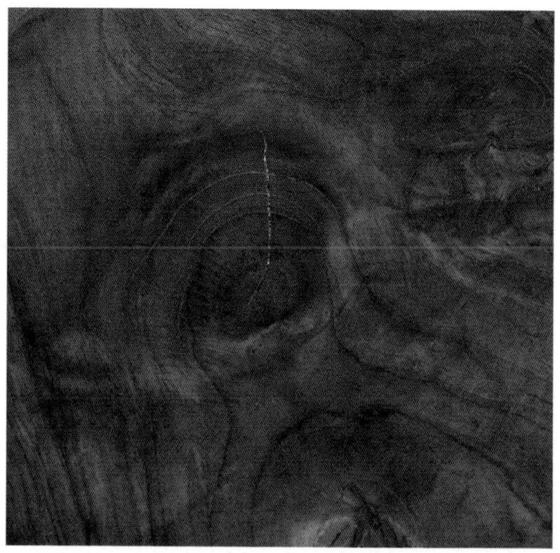

VISUAL RESPONSE

While smell and touch are important senses and likely play into our preference for wood, our experience of wood is most often visual; it is therefore not surprising that most research on wood is related to visual response. When we look at a piece of wood, much of what we are seeing is grain pattern and surface color. Researchers have looked at specific aspects of color and patterns to try to ascertain which we prefer.

Color, collinear lines and contours are the three main visual characteristics of wood that have shown evidence of contributing to why we love wood.

Photos: courtesy Pixabay and (lower right) Michael Bednar, courtesy naturallywood.com

ASSOCIATIVE/SEMANTIC PROCESSING

Research continues to indicate that nature-made and human-made objects and environments are processed differently in our brains. Humans subconsciously sort between natural and anthropogenic creations, and seem to prefer those that are nature-made (Vessel, 2018). While wooden objects are crafted by humans — a process that is often considered manufactured or unnatural — the wood itself is considered to be "natural" (Nyrud, 2015). Since there seems to be a preference for natural versus manufactured objects, it is possible that the brain makes that same link with wood when compared to highly processed materials like metals and plastics.

> In other words, the brain subconsciously links wood to trees, trees to life and nature and, thus, a biophilic response (Vessel, 2012).

One possible explanation for our biophilic response to wood is that the brain makes a series of associations — what is sometimes referred to as semantic processing. In other words, the brain subconsciously links wood to trees, trees to life and nature and, thus, a biophilic response (Vessel, 2012). This connection is somewhat implied by the work on associative processing (Vessel, 2018) and in general public surveys (Rametsteiner, 2007). It is a plausible explanation for our positive response to wood.

DESIGNING WITH WOOD

When using wood for a biophilic response there are several things to remember. The wood in a space should be visible, and having about 40-50 percent of the surfaces as wood seems to be optimal. There is a preference for warmer colored woods with some but not too many knots. Since much of the response is likely due to the collinear pattern of wood grain, avoid painting, staining or lacquering the wood in a way that hides the grain.

INTERPRETIVE PROCESSING AND MASS OBJECTS

How the visual cortex processes images, which are then interpreted in other parts of the brain, is an important part of the positive response to wood. One researcher has proposed that the brain sorts objects either by shape or by surface characteristics. The initial interpretive processing of an image sorts it by things that can be counted (like spheres, cones, cubes, and pyramids) versus things that are a mass (like sand, water, and wood). These mass objects are processed based on surface characteristics such as texture and color, rather than form or shape (Biederman, 1987). When the brain looks at wood, it (almost) instantaneously identifies the curves of the wood grain and surface appearance to determine the type of material. Whether the object is a chair, guitar, spatula, beam, or sheet of plywood, the brain identifies it as wood by the patterns on the surface.

The groves and knots that make up the surface pattern of wood have been the focus of a few studies suggesting that people prefer wood with a limited number of knots. Survey work indicates that a few knots are interesting, but an abundance of knots is disliked (Nakamura, 2007). Using eye-tracking systems to study how the eye moves across an image — recording when and where the eye stops on knots — shows that wood with many knots causes more eye stops (Nakamura, 2008).

This may mean that it takes more effort to process the image. The researchers noticed that the introduction of parallel, colored grooves distracted attention away from the knots. This begs the question of whether the calming and preference responses are due to the nature of wood grain itself.

COLLINEAR PATTERN PROCESSING

Wood grain is essentially a series of collinear stripes or grooves that are broken into segments to form nested contour patterns. Studies with rhesus monkeys indicate that images of lines running in the same direction are processed by the same set of neurons in the brain; whereas, with lines running in multiple directions, more effort is needed — by multiple sets of neurons — to process the image (Hubel, 1968). The brain will follow curvatures and contours (Li, 2002) and even connect short segments of lines to discern a longer curving pattern (Li, 2008). These pattern conditions occur frequently in nature and our brains, it could be argued, are predisposed to easily decipher them (Albright, 2002).

BIOPHILIC BENEFITS OF WOOD

There are a range of meaningful physiological and psychological benefits of being in a space with wood products and surfaces.

- Lowered blood pressure and lowered heart rate
- Increased activation of the parasympathetic nervous system/calming
- Perception of warmth
- Expressed visual preference for the space
- Perceived connection between wood and other living things

Photo: Nachelle Nocom/Unsplash

STATISTICAL FRACTALS

Fractals are layered self-repeating mathematical patterns. Exact fractals, which are the result of the same equation replicated at various scales, like embedded fractal gaskets or the Mandelbrot sets, don't occur in nature. However, when those mathematical patterns have variations, their ubiquity in nature becomes quite evident — snowflakes, fern leaves, waves on a beach, flames in a fireplace, the dappled light under trees. These are statistical fractals, and are so common that when we see these

The LEED Platinum office building in False Creek Flats in East Vancouver, British Columbia, features wood as structure, flooring, ceiling, and handrails, offering both visual and tactile experiences of wood without overwhelming the senses. Architect: Proscenium Architecture + Interiors, Inc. Photo: KK Law, courtesy naturallywood.com

patterns, even in human designed objects, it is easy for the brain to process the image and measurably lower our stress level (Hägerhäll, 2008, 2015). This effect is called fractal fluency (Abboushi, 2019).

We were not able to find research specifically studying wood grain as a fractal when writing this essay, but it could be argued that the nested contour patterns that are repeated in a wood grain fits the definition of a statistical fractal.

A year-long study on the results of minimal biophilic design interventions in a sixth-grade mathematics classroom found improved academic performance and better stress recovery responses among the students. The interventions included an enhanced garden outside the classroom, carpet tiles with a wavy prairie grass collinear pattern, a wallpaper frieze of abstracted palm leaves with biomorphic forms and collinear patterns, some wave form ceiling tiles, and fabric window blinds printed with the patterns of tree branch shadows that created statistical fractals (Determan, 2019). While not using wood as an intervention, the use of collinear patterns and statistical fractals were clearly important to outcomes.

Ultimately, we suspect that the main biophilic response to wood is due to the way the brain processes collinear and contour patterns, and potentially as a statistical fractal. Further pursuit of these research areas may just open our eyes to another level of value for wood products and materials in a Living Building.

REFERENCES

Abboushi, B., Elzeyadi, I., Taylor, R. S., & Sereno, M. (2019). Fractals in architecture: The visual interest, preference and mood response to projected fractal light patterns in interior spaces. ***Journal of Environmental Psychology, 61,*** 57-70. doi.org/10.1016/j.jenvp.2018.12.005

Albright, T. D., & Stoner, G. R. (2002). Contextual influences on visual processing. ***Annual Review of Neuroscience, 25***, 339-379. https://doi.org/10.1146/annurev.neuro.25.112701.142900

Biederman, I. (1987). Recognition-by-components: A theory of human understanding. ***Psychological Review, 94***(2), 115-147. doi.org/10.1037/0033-295X.94.2.115

Blackenberger, D., Van Den Wymelenberg, K., & Stenson, J. (2019). Visual effects of wood on thermal perception of interior environments. ***ARCC Conference Repository, 1***(1). Retrieved September 10, 2021, from www.arcc-journal.org/index.php/repository/article/view/619

Determan, J., Albright, T., Browning, W., Akers, M. A., Archibald, P., Martin-Dunlop, C. & Valerie Caruolo, V. (2019) 'The Impact of Biophilic Design on Student Success', AIA BRIK, November 2019.

Fell, D. R. (2010). Wood in the human environment: restorative properties of wood in the built indoor environment [Dissertation]. University of British Columbia, Vancouver. dx.doi.org/10.14288/1.0071305

Grote, V., Frühwirth, M., Lackner, H. K., Goswami, N., Köstenberger, M., Likar, R., & Moser, M. (2021). Cardiorespiratory interaction and autonomic sleep quality improve during sleep in beds made from Pinus cembra (Stone Pine) solid wood. ***Int. J. Environ. Res. Public Health, 18***(18), 9749. doi.org/10.3390/ijerph18189749

Hägerhäll, C. M., Laike, T., Taylor, R. S., Küller, M., Küller, R., & Martin, T. P. (2008). Investigations of human EEG response to viewing fractal patterns. ***Perception, 37,*** 1488-1494. doi.org/10.1068/p5918

Hägerhäll, C. M., Laike, T., Kuller, M., Marcheschi, E., Boydston, C. R., & Taylor, R. S. (2015). Human physiological benefits of viewing nature: EEG responses to exact and statistical fractal patterns. ***Nonlinear dynamics, psychology, and life sciences, 19***(1), 1-12.

Harada, H., Kashiwadani, H., Kanmura, Y., & Kuwaki, T. (2018). Linalool odor-induced anxiolytic effects in mice. ***Frontiers in Behavioral Neuroscience, 21***(241). doi.org/10.3389/fnbeh.2018.00241

Herz, R. S., (2004). Neuroimaging evidence for the emotional potency of odor-evoked memory. ***Neuropsychologia, 24***(3), 371-378. doi: 10.1016/j.neuropsychologia.2003.08.009

Hubel, D. H., & Wiesel, T. N. (1968). Receptive fields and functional architecture of monkey striate cortex. ***Journal of Physiology, 195***, 215-243, as cited in Gilbert, C. D. (2014). Intermediate-level visual processing and visual primitives (Chapter 27). In Kandel, E. R., Schwartz, J. H., Jessell, T. M., Siegelbaum, S. A., Hudspeth, A. J., & Mack, S. (Eds.). Principles of neural science (5th ed.). McGraw Hill.

Ikei, H., Song, C., & Miyazaki, Y. (2015). Physiological effect of olfactory stimulation by Hinoki cypress *(Chamaecyparis*

William Browning, BED Colorado University, MSRED MIT, Hon. AIA, LEED AP., is one of the green building industry's foremost thinkers. Terrapin Bright Green is an environmental strategies research and consulting firm. Browning's clients include Disney, New Songdo City, Lucasfilm, Google, Bank of America, Salesforce, CoStar, the US National Park Service, Marriott, the White House, Interface, and the Sydney 2000 Olympics. He has written a number of publications including, Green Development, The Economics of Biophilia, and Nature Inside. Browning was a founding board member of the USGBC.

TERRAPIN BRIGHT GREEN

Terrapin Bright Green is an environmental consulting and strategic planning firm committed to improving the human environment through high performance development, policy, and related research. Terrapin elevates conversations and helps clients to think creatively about environmental opportunities. Since 2006, Terrapin and its network of specialists have worked to shape the outcome of large-scale planning and design projects around the world. Terrapin has offices in New York City and Washington, DC, and works with private companies, public institutions, and government agencies on a variety of project types.

terrapinbrightgreen.com

obtusa) leaf oil. ***Journal of Physiological Anthropology, 34***(44). doi.org/10.1186/s40101- 015-0082-2

Ikei, H., Song, C., & Miyazaki, Y. (2017). Physiological effects of touching wood. ***International Journal of Environmental Research and Public Health, 14***(7), 801.

Li, W. & Gilbert, C. D. (2002). Global contour saliency and local colinear interactions. ***Journal of Neurophysiology, 88,*** 2846-56. doi.org/10.1152/jn.00289.2002

Li, W., Piech, V., & Gilbert, C. D. (2008). Learning to link visual contours. ***Neuron, 57,*** 442-451. doi.org/10.1016/j.neuron.2007.12.011

Morikawa, T., Miyazaki, Y., & Kobayashi, S. (1998). Time-series variations of blood pressure due to contact with wood. J of Wood Sci, 44, 495-497. doi. org/10.1007/BF00833417

Nakamura, M., & Kondo, T. (2007). Characterization of distribution pattern of eye fixation pauses in observation of knotty wood panel images. ***Journal of Physiological Anthropology, 26***(2), 129-133. doi.org/10.2114/jpa2.26.129

Nakamura, M., & Kondo, T. (2008). Quantification of visual inducement of knots by eye-tracking. ***Journal of Wood Science, 54***(1), 22-27. doi.org/10.1007/s10086-007-0910-z

Nyrud, A. Q., & Bringslimark, T. (2010). Is interior wood use psychologically beneficial? A review of psychological responses toward wood. ***Wood Fiber Science, 42***(2), 202-218. wfs.swst.org/index.php/wfs/article/view/1365

Rametsteiner, E., Oberhammer, R., & Gschwandtl, E. (2007). Europeans and wood: What do Europeans think about wood and its uses? A review of consumer and business surveys in Europe. Ministerial Conference on the Protection of Forests in Europe, Liaison Unit Warsaw, Poland. Retrieved August 14, 2021, from www.researchgate.net/publication/282573684

Rice, J., Kozak, R. A., Meitner, M. J., & Cohen, D. H. (2006). Appearance of wood products and psychological well-being. ***Wood and Fiber Science, 38***(4), 644-659. www.researchgate.net/publication/241779924

Ryan, C. O., Browning, W. D., Clancy, J. O., Andrews, S. L., & Kallianpurkar, N. B. (2014). Biophilic design patterns: Emerging nature-based parameters for health and well-being in the built environment. Archnet-IJAR: ***International Journal of Architectural Research, 8***(2), 62-76.

Sakuragawa, S., Miyazaki, Y., Kaneko, T., & Makita, T. (2005). Influence of wood wall panels on physiological and psychological responses. ***J of Wood Sci, 51,*** 136-140. doi. org/10.1007/s10086-004-0643-1

Sakuragawa, S., Kaneko, T., & Miyazaki, Y. (2008). Effects of contact with wood on blood pressure and subjective evaluation. ***J of Wood Sci, 54,*** 107-113. doi. org/10.1007/s10086-007-0915-7

Vessel, E. A., personal communication in 2012, while at New York University Center for Brain Imaging.

Vessel, E. A., Maurer, N., Denker, A. H., & Starr, G. G., (2018). Stronger shared taste for natural aesthetic domains than for artifacts of human culture. ***Cognition, 179***, 121-131. doi. org/10.1016/j.cognition.2018.06.009

Wilson, E. O. (1984). ***Biophilia.*** Cambridge, MA: Harvard University Press.

How Regenerative Wood Sourcing Helps Forests and Communities

Ryan Temple

Terry Campbell

Paul Vanderford

&

Trent Seager

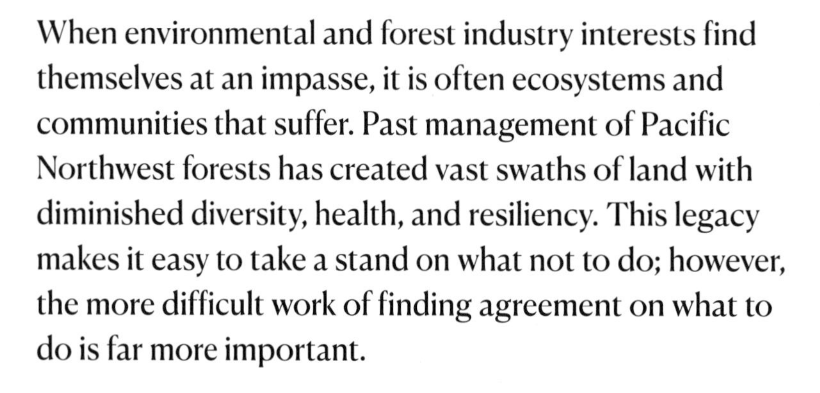

When environmental and forest industry interests find themselves at an impasse, it is often ecosystems and communities that suffer. Past management of Pacific Northwest forests has created vast swaths of land with diminished diversity, health, and resiliency. This legacy makes it easy to take a stand on what not to do; however, the more difficult work of finding agreement on what to do is far more important.

It is possible to source regional wood products that support both human economies and healthy forest ecosystems. Photo: courtesy Trout Mountain Forestry

As stakeholders are charting a path forward, they are looking not just at how to sustain forests but also at how to regenerate damaged ones. When regeneration includes the removal of trees, communities may also benefit. Sustainable Northwest has made the long-term investments in collaboration and trust-building that are needed to move projects forward. Their "radical middle" mantra requires people to envision a future where wood products and forest health depend on each other. As restorative forestry projects began, it became clear that markets could be a powerful driver of this work and that purchasing choices are critical to sustaining restoration work. A new type of business was needed to bridge restorative forestry and the market.

Fifteen years ago, Sustainable Northwest Wood opened, bringing sustainable, local building materials to market and educating design and construction professionals about how they can be used. SNW Wood provides a project team with Forest Stewardship Council (FSC) certified products or products from other restorative practices; however, some project teams may seek a deeper understanding of the opportunities in the industry to create a regenerative relationship between our forestland and their projects.

Recognizing the importance of defining ecological regenerative forestry and educating large-scale customers on why and how to source from it, the non-profit Sustainable Northwest's Green Markets Program works on procurement policies, wood source tracking, and source verification. The resulting cooperation along the supply chain enables projects to connect back to specific forest management practices and tell a compelling story about the people and places that it supports.

Together, Sustainable Northwest Green Markets and Sustainable Northwest Wood offer multiple pathways for achieving regenerative building through local wood product purchasing.

Their complementary work is summarized as follows:

Sustainable Northwest Wood (SNW Wood) is a for-profit construction material supplier that can deliver their products to any market in the United States. Their on-staff experts are knowledgeable about regenerative land management as it pertains to their products.

Sustainable Northwest - Green Markets is a non-profit organization that can help clients design wood procurement strategies that meet their values. They can track the wood products that arrive on project jobsites and use storytelling to help spread the word about the projects' successes.

While these two entities work at different intersections within the design and construction industry, their work is complementary to the industry as a whole. The following case studies demonstrate how they work together to deliver some of the most ambitious projects in the Western United States.

Photo: Terry Campbell

EQUITABLE SOURCING: MEYER MEMORIAL TRUST HEADQUARTERS IN PORTLAND, OREGON

Meyer Memorial Trust's mission is to work with and invest in organizations, communities, ideas, and efforts that contribute to a flourishing and equitable Oregon. The construction of Meyer's headquarters provided an opportunity to use construction choices — specifically, intentional wood procurement — as a vehicle for advancing the foundation's mission. SNW and Meyer created wood sourcing criteria that recognize and support forests managed for human health, water, wildlife habitat, carbon sequestration, and worker rights. Additionally, Meyer committed to supporting rural forestry-based jobs, rural communities, and innovation in Oregon by building with local wood. The approach focuses on achieving the greatest positive impact and requires transparency to understand both the forests and the people who produce the wood products.

Priorities included:

- Supporting local forests, mills, and jobs.
- Buying wood products linked to forest restoration, reclaimed sources, or FSC-certified operations.
- Preferred contracting with BIPOC-owned forests and businesses.

The three-story, 20,000-square-foot building used wood for the following twelve building elements: flooring, siding, decking, cabinets and casework, framing, glulam beams, roof trusses, interior doors, trim and baseboard, acoustic ceiling, joists, and mass plywood panels. Ten of these products were purchased in Oregon; nine products were tracked back to sustainably managed forests; and seven were sourced from minority-owned or small businesses. At 3 percent ($24,650 of a $754,000 total wood package), the premium paid to ensure the project's wood product procurement achieved Meyer's community, equity and conservation goals was minimal.

FULL TRANSPARENCY OF CHANGED LANDSCAPES: THE NATURE CONSERVANCY (TNC) HEADQUARTERS IN PORTLAND, OREGON

When The Nature Conservancy decided to remodel their Oregon headquarters, the organization prioritized the use of wood that reflected their conservation values. To accomplish this goal, their team reached out to Sustainable Northwest Wood and asked if it would be possible to use only FSC-certified wood. The answer was yes. However, as we began to learn more about the project, we recognized an opportunity to go even further. Having been approached early in the project meant that we could pinpoint the sources of products that would match their needs and aspirations.

Because Juniper is sourced from High Desert rangeland restoration projects, TNC was interested in it as a siding product. The design team was not aware that there was a planned rangeland restoration project taking place on the Nature Conservancy's very own Juniper Hills Preserve. Sustainable Northwest Wood was able to coordinate the logging, milling, and finishing of the Juniper siding so that the wood could be traced back to its place of origin. This approach required a little more work but no additional cost. Interestingly, "rangeland restoration" does not neatly fit within the sustainable forestry criteria of the Forest Stewardship Council. With rangeland restoration, the goals are to restore native sage steppe habitat, rehabilitate watersheds, and promote soil conservation. For this

customer, achieving specific labeling criteria was not as important as truly understanding the ecological impacts of the material and tying those to a precise location.

Every stick of siding and fencing in the new Oregon Conservation Center is directly linked back to regenerative practices on Nature Conservancy lands. As an added bonus, when the Oregon TNC office lamented that they did not have a source for their cedar decking that could match this story, SNW Wood let them know that the Washington branch of TNC was about to implement old-growth restoration work on their Ellsworth Creek preserve that would yield a handful of smaller cedar trees. We were able to secure these logs and track them through the supply chain right up until the cedar planks were screwed down on the rooftop deck.

CELEBRATING REGIONAL FORESTRY: PDX TERMINAL CORE

Acquiring 3 million board feet of lumber to remodel a fourteen-acre working airport terminal is an ambitious enough project that the Port of Portland could have been forgiven if they had sourced that wood from wherever they could find it; however, the Port saw an opportunity to celebrate the best of regional forestry, channel revenue back into local communities, and showcase a diversity of landowners and mills that represent the vanguard of regenerative practices.

Rather than restrict sustainable sourcing to specific labels, the Port opted to focus on outcomes. Criteria were set that considered how long trees were allowed to grow, emphasized what is left behind as opposed to what is cut, and tracked desired outcomes such as old-growth regeneration and forest resiliency. Despite naysayers, Sustainable Northwest Wood affirmed that the project goals could be met, and that wood could be tracked from the roof all the way back to the forest where it had grown.

The new terminal at the PDX airport in Portland, Oregon, demonstrates how regional sourcing can support local communities and support sustainable forest practices.

In total, 600,000 BF of beautiful 3x6 Douglas-fir for the roof lattice were sourced meeting the following criteria:

- FSC certification, ensuring wood was sourced from well-managed forests with all the associated carbon sequestering benefits.
- Traceable back to local forest of origin with an emphasis on supporting a diversity of landowner types, including Public, Tribal, Community and Small Family.
- Local milling to create jobs and revenue within a circular economy.
- Competitive pricing compared to wood sourced without adherence to the above criteria.

In addition, 2,000,000 BF of 2x8 Douglas-fir for the glulam beams supporting the roof were sourced with similar high-level goals and achieved the following outcomes:

- Supply chain transparency back to primary mills.
- Log sourcing information from primary mills summarizing their log purchasing.
- 350,000 BF of the lumber used in glulam stock was sourced from Yakama Forest Products, a mill that directly supports forest stewardship and restoration work on the Yakama Indian Reservation.
- FSC Certification for all wood fiber that could not be directly traced and field verified.

landscapes, we will have to figure out how to replicate this approach. We recommend adopting the following strategies when sourcing wood:

1. Set goals early on and adhere to them. Planning is critical. The front-end work will foster both commitment and collaboration among those involved.

2. Bring atypical stakeholders to the table. Though it is not common for project leads to visit forests and mills, providing even limited opportunities to do so will build mutual understanding and respect that will facilitate cooperation.

3. Educate and inspire all team members about the importance and impact of sourcing.

The purchase of this wood directly supported hundreds of acres of restoration work. Post-harvest, these forests will be more resilient to drought, fire, insects, and disease and will have improved stand structure, habitat values, light access, and water availability. The project proved that wood procurement can go beyond "less harmful" to having a net-positive impact on the landscape.

Though the benefits to communities and forests from this project are significant, if we are to realize exponential benefits across

4. Engage deeply with the regional supply chain and seek partners who are well versed in regenerative efforts. The standard lumber supply chain is not designed with sustainability and source tracking in mind. Working with suppliers like Sustainable Northwest Wood will not only help project teams achieve their goals, it will also foster a gratifying experience as project owners, managers, and laborers come to know about the people and places that supply their wood.

River Sol, a residential project in Bend, Oregon, features locally milled and salvaged cedar siding and FSC-certified framing lumber. Photo: courtesy Tozer Design

FSC-CERTIFIED SOURCING FOR A LIVING BUILDING: RIVER SOL IN BEND, OREGON

The River Sol project is a newly built private residence in Bend, Oregon that is seeking full Living Building Challenge certification. This requires the project to meet the Materials Petal, with its intent "to help create a materials economy that is non-toxic, ecologically restorative and transparent." Al Tozer of Tozer Design reached out to Sustainable Northwest Wood early in the process, as he knew that one of the Petal's most challenging aspects is the requirement to build with FSC-certified products. FSC-certified building materials meet all of the Materials Petal's intent; it is the only forest certification system that truly requires forestland owners to manage to a higher standard than state and federal law would require. In the process of managing forests to this standard, forestland owners are restoring ecosystems to be more resilient to future fires, climate change, and pests.

Most architects would start designing the project with the best building materials available, but Tozer's experience with Desert Rain House, Bend's other full Living Building Challenge project, gave him a reason to approach this project design in a different way. Al knew that not all building materials are available from FSC-certified mills, so a project that needed to use only FSC-certified wood products should

RESTORATION FORESTRY

Restoration Forestry is a proactive forest management tool that aims to recover degraded forest landscapes. Some examples of ecological restoration activities in forests include thinning forests and harvesting small patches of trees in single-species "plantations" that developed after the harvest of old-growth trees to create a more varied forest composition. Research has shown that restoration within wet coastal forests can increase the spacing of overstory trees, allowing for growth more characteristic of older stands, while increasing the amount of sunlight that reaches the forest floor. Increased light supports an increase in ground vegetation, which provides food for many different types of animals.

Research also shows that restoration of dry forests can improve fire behavior, water capture, habitat value, and, in some cases, provide economically valuable sawlogs. Restoration can increase site moisture by 10-30 percent, contributing to stream flow during low flow summer periods critical to salmon recovery. Treatments can also lessen the intensity and destructiveness of wildfire. Management achieves this by increasing stand diversity — variation in the age, size and spacing of trees — and by selecting for fire tolerant species like Ponderosa Pine.

be designed with readily available FSC-certified products up front. For example, engineered wood products such as I-joists, laminated veneer lumber (LVL), and parallel strand lumber (PSL) are common building materials that architects and builders use every day; however, none of them are available from FSC-certified mills. Consequently, staff from SNW Wood redirected Al's design toward FSC-certified building materials that were available, including full sawn, solid Doug-fir beams and glulams.

Another challenge was the lack of an FSC Chain of Custody (COC)-certified roof truss manufacturer in the region. SNW Wood was able to use its FSC Outsourcing Agreement with the builder's preferred non-FSC truss manufacturer. This process required SNW Wood to buy the correct amount of FSC lumber upfront and provide it to the truss manufacturer so they could identify it, segregate it and run it as its own batch. This approach eliminated the possibility of co-mingling FSC materials with non-FSC lumber at the facility.

For the inexperienced or uninformed, the challenges of sourcing FSC-certified products to meet the Materials Petal can seem daunting, but the River Sol project demonstrates that when the full project team — including the architect, builder and client — is on board, new pathways of thinking can help increase the success of projects. Plus, it helps to have a material supplier who is knowledgeable, committed, and passionate about making these projects work.

Ryan Temple is the founder of Sustainable Northwest Wood, a B-Corp providing sustainably sourced forest products for the full range of building needs. The most fulfilling aspect of his job is spending time in the communities and landscapes that are positively impacted by the company's customers.

Terry Campbell began his career in the sustainable wood products industry in 2000 with the Certified Forest Products Council. In 2004, he started a consulting practice focused on training, certification expertise and marketing for sustainable wood product companies. Joining Sustainable Northwest Wood in 2014 he now works on creating markets for wood products that protect ecosystem services, provide rural economic development, and connect people to place.

Paul Vanderford has a degree in Natural Resource Management and sixteen years experience building markets that recognize and reward wood products connected to forest stewardship in all forms. As Green Markets Director at Sustainable Northwest Paul's work uses transparency, data, and relationships with forest owners and market partners to help project teams align purchasing with either equity, climate, and economic goals. Paul is a founding member of the Climate Smart Wood Group and works as a wood advisor for tech clients, municipalities, private development and affordable housing partners. Paul's work provides options for the building community to have a positive footprint by purchasing wood products in support of landscape resilience and other climate solutions.

Trent Seager has a PhD in Forest Ecology and more than twenty years experience working in the natural resources field. Currently, he serves as the Director of Science for Sustainable Northwest, where he has worked for more than five years. Trent works with Tribal Nations, National Forests, and rural communities across Oregon and Washington by providing science support and ecological context to help highlight solutions in forest restoration to provide wildlife habitat, water quality, forest structure, and resilient landscapes with restored ecological processes and functions.

Footprint, Handprint: Pursuing Regenerative Architecture in Rwanda

Kelly Alvarez Doran

&

James Kitchin

Over the past fifteen years, MASS Design Group has developed an approach to design and construction that focuses on minimizing a project's ecological and carbon footprint whilst maximizing its human handprint. We have come to understand that a regenerative project requires a holistic approach to defining both its performance as well as its provenance — that a building's impacts extend well beyond its site boundaries to include where materials are sourced and processed, and the hands through which they pass.

The Rwanda Institute for Conservation Agriculture (RICA) demonstrates how the hyper-local sourcing of materials can dramatically drive down a project's carbon footprint.

Our recognition that a building has both a footprint and a handprint emerged organically. MASS began as a small group of architects working with Partners in Health (PIH) and the Government of Rwanda to design and construct a hospital in a rural, un-electrified, underserved part of the country. Fifteen years ago, Rwanda was investing in its reconstruction from the 1994 genocide. The country focused on its health sector as a core building block and was eager to innovate and create examples for development rather than replicate previous (and often imported) models. Designing and building in such a context required us to leave our assumptions behind and unlearn the systems of global supply we have unconsciously relied on. We had to figure out how to source both materials and labor as regionally as possible in response to the constraints of the project's remote location in a landlocked country with an 18 percent import tax.

PIH tasked us to look at every decision as an opportunity to create a positive impact in the communities we were privileged to serve. That mandate pushed us to look at the project's immediate context as the *terroir* of design decision making, a lesson that has since become our philosophy. In place of a product catalog of materials and suppliers, we instead relied on a close reading of the region's material vernacular and the wisdom of local builders and craftspeople. Butaro Hospital's innovation is a result of its constraints and context: wards designed to function in the absence of electricity; walls built from the stones surfacing in surrounding fields; stones shaped and laid by the hands of Butaro's incredible masons.

A few years later, the African Wildlife Foundation invited us to design and build a primary school for the community of Ilima. Ilima is located in the center of the Democratic Republic of the Congo (DRC) — a geographic and logistic reality that made getting materials to the project site expensive, time consuming, and difficult. All imported materials and tools would spend a few weeks traveling up river from Kinshasa to Mompono; from there, they would be transported along a road no wider than your shoulders — at points on the back of a dirt bike — for the better part of four hours in each direction. Drawing on the lessons learned from PIH and Butaro, we focused our attention on Ilima; specifically, who is there,

Figure 1. Carbon Axon Diagram comparing the embodied carbon in a conventional building with the Rwanda Institute for Conservation Agriculture.

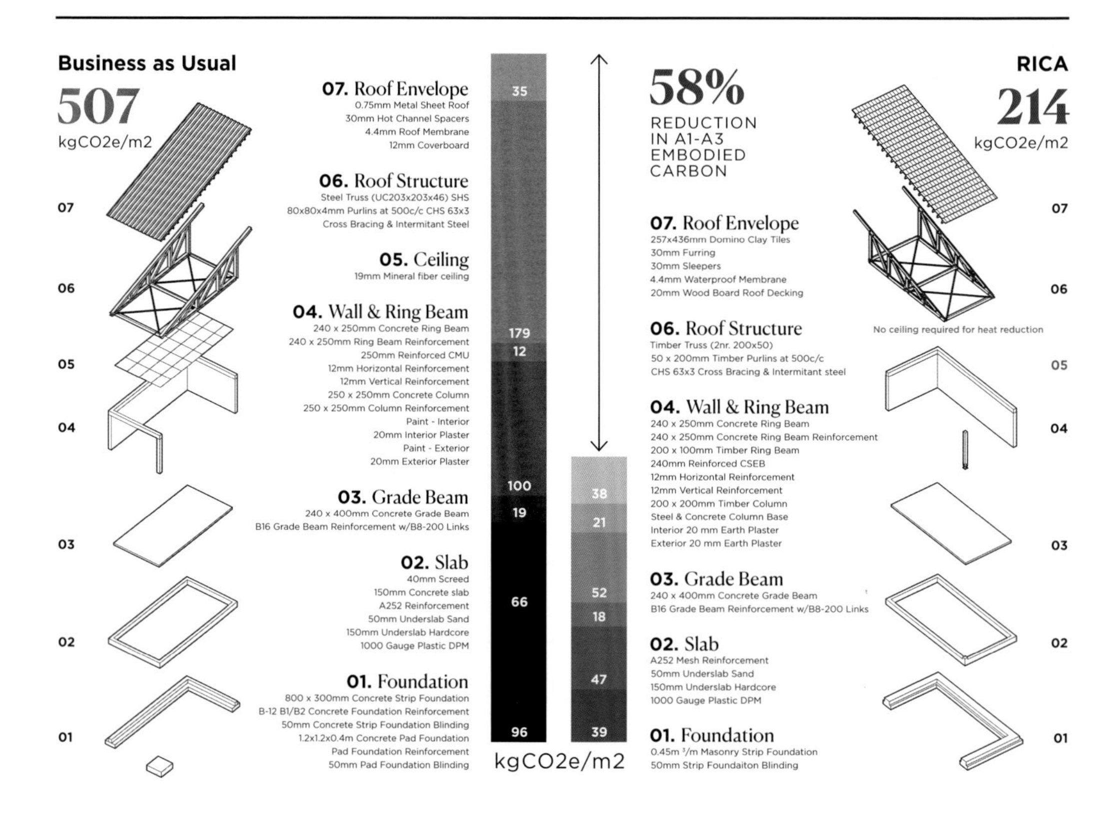

how do they build, what do they build with, and what materials are available in abundance? Our team spent weeks on the ground interviewing local craftspeople, collecting material samples, and working with the community to establish a site for the school.

On return to Kigali we sent the materials — primarily soils and wood samples — to a lab to help determine their suitability for structural and finish applications. We discovered that the soils harvested from multiple termite mounds surrounding the site provided an ideal mix for a robust, sun-dried block that could form the exterior walls of the school. An endemic hardwood (African Padauk) shares traits with cedar, enabling it to withstand rain and rot, and it could be cleaved and shaped with a froe to provide a durable, easily replaceable roofing system. Ilima Primary School is ultimately a result of local knowledge and lab testing, the alchemy of our commitment to seeking innovation grounded in the specifics of a place and its people.

Ilima Primary School was also our first attempt to thoroughly audit the socio-economic and environmental impacts of the projects. Our role as architect, engineer, construction manager, and procurement officer provided a detailed accounting of both costs and quantities. Sourcing 99 percent of the building's weight from within a ten-kilometer radius allowed 74 percent of the project's construction budget to make its way into the immediate communities. Harvesting stone, soils, and woods from the immediate context meant that 83 percent of the budget was put in the hands of project labor, with only 17 percent required to purchase tools, fasteners, and limited amounts of cement for the foundations.

Ilima was also our introduction into quantifying the upfront impacts of construction. We worked with researchers at Massachusetts Institute of Technology (MIT) to explore the embodied carbon of our projects for the first time. The results shocked us. The building's carbon footprint (15 kg CO_2e/m^2) was twenty-eight times lower than the global average for schools due entirely to the reliance on locally sourced stone, earth and wood. This small school, built of locally abundant and readily renewable materials in the middle of DRC, provided us our first glimpse of the potential for a regenerative, climate-positive architecture.

Soon thereafter, we were presented with an opportunity to push the limits of a design process that focused on minimizing the carbon footprint whilst maximizing its human handprint. In 2016, Howard G. Buffett Foundation invited us to help them envision, design, and build from the ground up a university focused on educating the next generation of agricultural innovators. Howard's investment in agricultural

An aerial view of the Rwanda Institute for Conservation Agriculture, or RICA.

education reflects his deep belief in small-scale farming as a fundamental component of addressing long-term food security and peace worldwide. The conception of the Rwanda Institute for Conservation Agriculture (RICA) is thus grounded in an education of small-farm realities: providing the conditions for its students and researchers to scale innovations that leverage human capital and creativity as the primary means of increasing agricultural yield and economic value.

One Health is rooted in the understanding that the health of one community is inextricably linked with those around it, and that all systems flourish through an exchange of ideas, energy, and matter.

We proposed a "One Health" approach — a holistic design method that seeks to balance and optimize the health of people, animals, and ecosystems. One Health is rooted in the understanding that the health of one community is inextricably linked with those around it, and that all systems flourish through an exchange of ideas, energy, and matter. To begin understanding these exchanges, our first step once again required investing in an extended immersion of the site and the surrounding communities of people, plants, and animals. Conducting workshops with local communities to assess material and labor practices also cultivated

a deeper understanding of the area's unique social, ecological, and agricultural history.

We discovered that the 1,200-hectare site that had functioned as a Ministry of Agriculture testing site was previously a national park, one of only two in Rwanda's savannah region. Working with Rwanda's foremost ecologist, we undertook a detailed ecological survey that identified a series of threatened endemic plant and bird species in the largest remaining intact savannah woodland in southern Rwanda. The plan for the campus builds around existing biodiversity and seeks to heal the landscape by stitching together habitats and agricultural spaces.

The large site also provided the grounds for achieving a climate-positive project. Our team of architects and engineers worked to reduce the upfront embodied impacts of the project to 40 percent of a business-as-usual case by harvesting much of the project's materials from the site itself and by reducing the use of carbon-intensive materials like cement and steel as much as possible. To reduce operational emissions, we worked with Transsolar and Arup to optimize RICA for daylighting, natural ventilation, and water efficiency to reduce demands, thus reducing the size of the solar farm and water treatment facilities that support the off-grid campus. This results in a dramatically reduced life cycle carbon footprint — one that can be offset on-site through twenty years of afforestation and silviculture — which will result in Africa's first climate-positive campus.

Can architecture be regenerative? To become so we need to understand our reciprocal relationship with nature: to take only what is given and what we need; to acknowledge that we have damaged the earth and that it needs healing. Is RICA regenerative? In some ways it heals. Using local knowledge, forty hectares of previously degraded farmland are being restored to savannah woodland, and through carbon sequestration in the forest, at least the climate change impacts of this project will be compensated for by 2040. Materials are inherently emissive, but we can reduce our footprint through intimate knowledge of the places we work, and we can maximize our handprint when we co-create with the people who live there.

ASSESSING HANDPRINTS AND FOOTPRINTS AT RICA

Over four years, we were able to engage over 800 people to build and fit-out the RICA campus, 90 percent of whom live in the surrounding Bugasera district. The project developed a supply chain of materials and finishes that were harvested, sourced, processed, and crafted locally. Ninety-six percent of the materials were sourced within Rwanda, which is slightly smaller than the state of Massachusetts. Of these materials, we chose to present the handprint and footprint of the stone, earth, and wood used in the project.

STONE

So much of a contemporary building's impact is buried underground, out of sight and out of mind, in the form of reinforced concrete foundations — the building's footprint in every respect. Traditional stone mortared foundations are a time-tested, local alternative. At RICA, the quartzite stone was quarried from within ten miles of the site. Each stone was individually placed in an interlocking pattern and caringly mortared by hand. A reinforced concrete grade beam ties the foundation together and resolves bending forces resulting from seismic activity. This foundation solution reduces embodied carbon by 60 percent compared to fully reinforced concrete solutions.

EARTH

The feasibility of earth as a building material is demonstrated by the thousands through Rwanda's vernacular housing. However, construction at the scale of a project like RICA required a rigorous approach to address durability and strength. During conceptual design, our in-house geotechnical and structural engineers dug pits across the site to identify the ideal soil mix for compressed stabilized earth blocks (CSEBs) and rammed earth. Drawing on our knowledge of the land and support from ecologists, we dug in the least ecologically sensitive areas to minimize impact. Through this early phased-testing approach, we optimized the soil mix by adding 4.5 percent Portland cement and 2.5 percent pozzolana (volcanic ash). These amendments significantly improved the durability and compressive strength of the blocks and allowed construction to continue during the rainy season without temporary shelters.

Approximately 2.5 million handmade CSEBs were made on the project site, accounting for 25 percent of total building material. The CSEB walls reduce embodied carbon by 50 percent compared to the more regionally typical concrete block walls. In addition to the invisible climate change benefits, the structure's thermal mass and hygrothermal properties help create a noticeably more pleasant indoor environment during hot, stormy savannah days.

EARTH (cont.)

Earth, in this context, is a hyper-local material. In five minutes, one can walk from the extraction pit to the canopy under which 60 workers manually press blocks, to the storage shed where thousands of blocks gain their strength, and finally, to the buildings where they are laid. We hypothesize that local material production leads to greater efficiency, reduced waste, and less harm, because witnessing production processes — mining, tree felling, and toxic manufacturing, which often leaches chemicals into the water or fills the sky and our noses with smoke — creates an emotional response and visceral connection to materials.

RICA demonstrates that earth buildings can be built beautifully, safely, and with minimal environmental impact at an industrial scale. Following the project, MASS supported the Government of Rwanda in the development of a standard and guidelines to improve the quality of the two million adobe homes forecasted to be constructed in coming decades.

WOOD

The design of this campus coincided with the first FSC forest management certification in Rwanda. With the idea that architecture is built for and by the place, we worked with the materials that were available through this regional mill, which does not ordinarily produce wood for construction. We built the structural grid with Patula Pine; however, the significant variation in dimensions, quality and volume of wood we received from the mill led us to supplement the supply from other forests. Unfortunately, there were no other regional FSC-certified forests that could meet our needs, which led to the challenging decision to work with a Tanzanian forest that was then seeking FSC certification. After investigating their forestry management practices in person, we determined it was better to support a fledgling sustainable forestry industry than to rely on imported steel members.

Mechanical grading is not currently performed at local mills, so our structural engineers trained personnel to visually grade the wood by assessing knot area ratios and locations. Additionally, we performed supplemental laboratory testing which demonstrated some members performed well below the weakest structural grade that would be assumed in the United Kingdom. When the wood arrived on site, our engineers performed a second visual grading and sorted members so that the strongest ones were used in the most highly utilized locations.

ACKNOWLEDGEMENTS

We would like to acknowledge the enormous team of engineers, architects, and builders who have and continue to work tirelessly to make this highly impactful project a reality. Thank you to our partners Arup, Transsolar, Atelier 10, and the collective that is MASS. And finally, thank you to our project partners; Partners in Health, The African Wildlife Foundation, and the Howard G. Buffett Foundation.

Kelly Alvarez Doran OAA MRAIC is a father, architect, educator, and environmental activist. As Senior Director of Performance and Provenance at MASS Design Group, Kelly supports Principals and Designers to embed environmental objectives into all MASS projects, as well as leading climate-focused research and the training of our entire team. Previously, Kelly led MASS's' Kigali office overseeing the growth of the practice from a team of eight to eighty over five years. He led the design and implementation of several of MASS's projects across East Africa, notably the award-winning Munini District Hospital and Rwanda Ministry of Health's Typical Hospital Plans; Nyarugenge District Hospital, headquarters for One Acre Fund and Andela in Kenya; and the Rwanda Institute for Conservation Agriculture. Kelly holds professorships at The Bartlett and the University of Toronto, where his Ha/f Research Studio focuses on the whole life carbon of the built environment. The outcomes of this research have informed the ongoing development of embodied carbon policies for the City of Toronto and surrounding municipalities.

James Kitchin CEng MICE has a background in structural and civil engineering and deep expertise in designing with healthy, natural, and non-conventional materials. He has written several articles on the subject, and has led research and policy change around building materials and embodied carbon. James strives to minimise the footprint of the built environment through intimate knowledge of place and process, and to maximize the maker's handprint through collaboration. As co-lead of the Performance & Provenance department at MASS, he is committed to imagining, advocating and implementing regenerative practices.

MASS DESIGN GROUP

MASS Design Group was founded on the understanding that architecture's influence reaches beyond individual buildings. Our mission is to research, build, and advocate for architecture that promotes justice and human dignity. MASS (Model of Architecture Serving Society) believes that architecture has a critical role to play in supporting communities to confront history, shape new narratives, collectively heal and project new possibilities for the future. We are a team of over 200 architects, landscape architects, engineers, builders, furniture designers, makers, writers, filmmakers, and researchers representing twenty countries across the globe. We believe in expanding access to design that is purposeful, healing, and hopeful.

Advocacy is Critical for Advancing Regenerative Materials

Charley Stevenson

Today, as recognition of advocacy's pivotal role in advancing sustainability grows, I am reminded — after myriad twists and turns — that my personal journey into healthier materials work also began with advocacy.

On behalf of a Living Building Challenge project for our first large client, Williams College, a colleague and I at my then-nascent company, Integrated Eco Strategy, spent countless hours calling manufacturers, outlining the Living Building Challenge, explaining why our questions mattered, and assuring them that we needed answers so that our team could make informed decisions. We diligently logged results on spreadsheets to track the data. It was serendipitous that Williams was the client, as it was one of the few institutions with

Integrated Eco Strategy consulted on all Imperatives of the Living Building Challenge on the Class of 1966 Environmental Center at Williams College in Williamstown, MA,. This was the first historic renovation project for the International Living Future Institute. Photo: Nick Noyes/IES

both the foresight and the commitment for undertaking what was then such a laborious task. We seriously underbid the job and ended up spending more than six hours on each of the hundreds of products that we researched for the project.

Projects two, three and four helped us hone our approach. We built a network we could tap into; we shortened our pitch; and we shaved minutes, then hours from our average product. All the while, we hoped that interest in healthier materials would scale rapidly. That happened with project number five, a building for Harvard University. It was a bold endeavor: screening all of the products in a massive, complex project. It was also a generous act by Harvard — to underwrite the task of researching thousands of products for a half-million square foot science and engineering laboratory, at a time when researching an especially challenging single product could take ten hours.

Now, reflecting on well more than a decade of sustainability consulting and software development, it's striking that — though we have reduced our research time and expense exponentially — the more data we compile, the more we know how much we do not know. A couple of aspects, though, are clear. Securing manufacturers' product transparency is the foundation of assessing all of the aspects of sustainability — health, carbon, social justice, and circularity. Advocacy is how we get there.

Ours was a process of education and discovery: we began to understand the market, while manufacturers learned about the Living Building Challenge and the vision for a future of responsible, transparent and healthy building products. Occasionally, we discovered a great product: simple ingredients, a manufacturer who knew the product's chemistry, and who was willing to share. Typically, these winning products were made with natural ingredients or produced in small shops. Made-in-

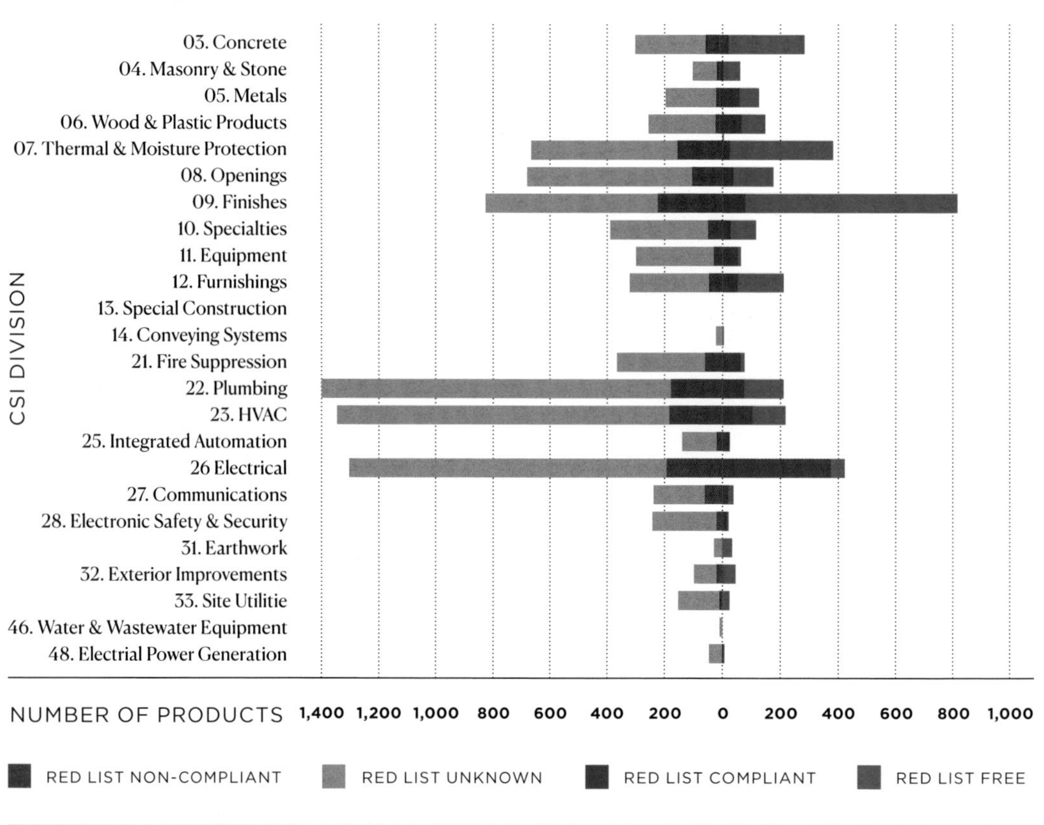

Figure 1. Information and solutions are unevenly distributed among the CSI divisions. A decade of advocacy prompted great strides in paints and other finishes, but plumbing, HVAC and electrical products have proven more difficult to improve. Understanding this distribution by division helps guide product choices and more accurately target advocacy efforts.

Figure 2. How data drives action: Understanding both product prevalence and overall product impact — not always strictly related — helps guide effective, efficient materials selection. Balancing prevalence and impact with relative levels of disclosure and Red List status lets researchers home in on the likeliest strategy for a given product type.

Strategy by Product Type

Advocacy

Engage with manufacturers; seek:

- Public disclosure @100ppm +
- Red List Free Ingredients

Disclosure

Choose products with public disclosure @100ppm:

- Declare +
- HPD

Optimization

Choose the best product in the product type:

- Public Disclosure @100ppm +
- Red List Free Ingredients

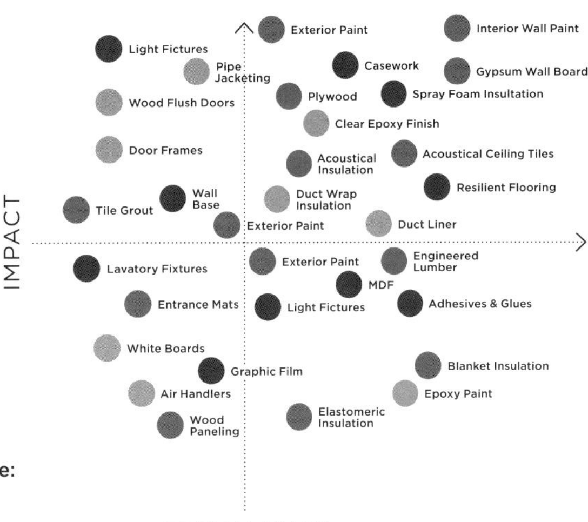

Massachusetts water tanks and a linseed oil-based wood filler were among the first such finds. As we learned about the filler and its formula, unchanged since the late 1800s, we traded emails with a sales manager whose AOL account indicated a similar devotion to tradition.

Through this outreach, IES began to build relationships in the building products marketplace, finding allies who were game to substitute a PVC-free cord or make our client a run of fixtures without a plastic finish of uncertain composition. As we learned, our focus shifted from comprehending products to reusing the best products that we had discovered to date. Initially, manufacturer affidavits were our stock in trade. By cultivating relationships with technical product representatives, we obtained partial product data (often privately, perhaps with a non-disclosure agreement). At this stage we had no choice but to accept that their claims of Red List free status — if they were willing to put them to paper — were better than nothing and good enough to move forward in a project. A pinky swear, but with documentation.

At this point in the evolution of our Living Building Challenge materials vetting process, these compliance determinations were nearly always made under time pressure. Healthier materials consultants were generally brought late to the dance, well after the bulk of the team was assembled and most or all of the design and product selection was complete. Consultants played a continual game of catch up. A submittal was overdue, a trade partner was champing at the bit: someone at IES had to say *right now* whether the project could risk using the product in question, despite imperfect knowledge.

Figure 3. Improvement requires continual advocacy, which is targeted and refined by amassing data on transparency, ingredients and other sustainability information. Production of better products is spurred by project teams buying the best materials currently available while advocating to manufacturers whose products fall short.

Improving Over Time

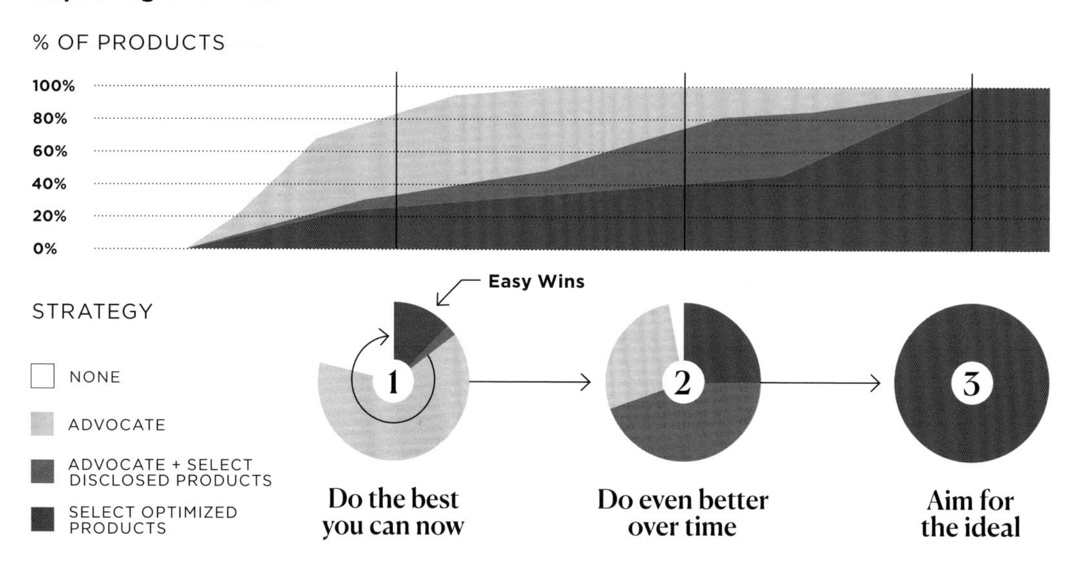

Under time pressure and in the absence of optimal products, it's easy to view advocacy as simply a vital lifeline, the only way to do what had to be done immediately while, we hoped, teeing up a better future. What was less apparent then, but surely is now, is that while finding and using a fully optimized product warms the heart, advocacy does the real work. It is with each challenging ingredient and every fruitful act of advocacy that fundamental changes can occur.

At about this time, the number of Health Product Declarations and Declare labels began to grow significantly. This was exciting — progress! — and also concerning: will we be out of consulting work because our advocacy had been so effective that the entire building products market would rush to furnish complete, trustworthy disclosures? Admittedly, the latter point was more aspirational than concerning. However, the comparative flood of information created a new issue — how do we store, manage and assess the data? Spreadsheets, we quickly realized, were a one-off proposition: difficult enough to manage on a single project; quite impossible to use to inform subsequent building projects. We began developing a materials management program and hiring and training a cadre of researchers — dubbed "healthy materials specialists" — to use it.

Training our new research team to use the new software and research products turned out to be the easy part. In our rural area, we have an abundance of bright talented citizens but, typically, a dearth of interesting and challenging jobs. Throw in a chance to

Figure 4. Product transparency in the materials marketplace has undergone more than two decades of continual improvement, prompted by LEED and spurred higher by stringent LBC requirements. Establishing reasonable goals, choosing the best products and, perhaps most important, conducting continual, effective advocacy, results in measurable improvements — leading to ever-higher aims and accomplishments.

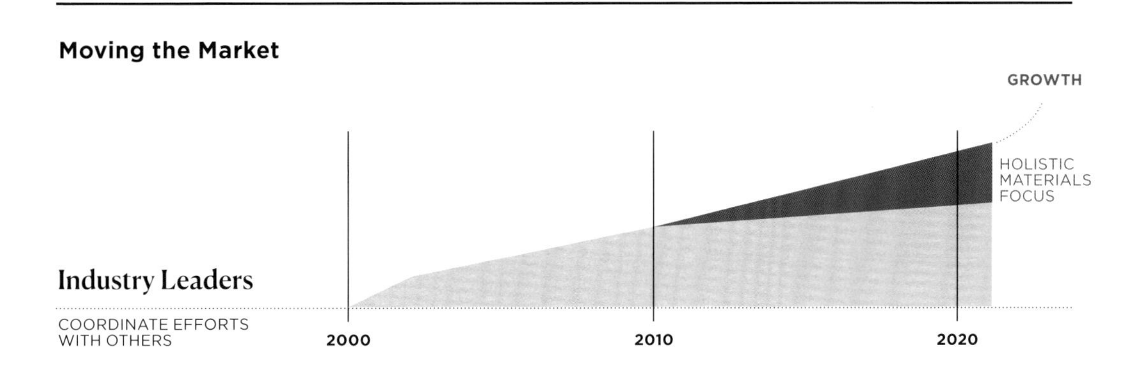

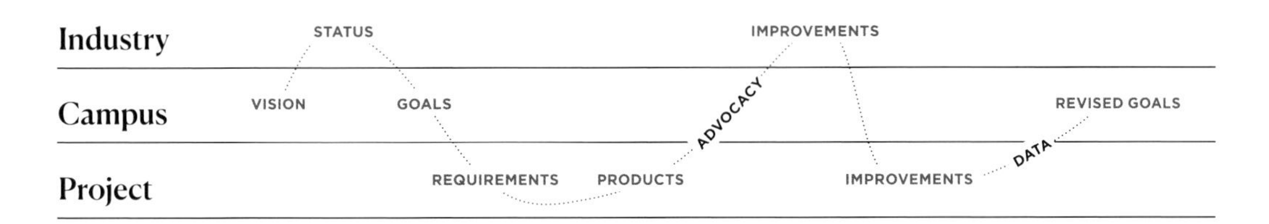

save the world and we soon assembled an industrious and tireless team who would, if left to it, pursue ingredient disclosure on a product until folks were living and working in the building for which it was intended. Deciding where to draw the line on product approvals — defining and hewing to "good enough" — prompted long debate and conjecture. Over time, we shifted the focus from obtaining every single available detail on a product to efficiently declaring a given material's research "complete" and sharpening our advocacy outreach. This evolution was essential, and it is what we do today.

Private claims of Red List free products were growing, but we realized that we were fast approaching a dead end of our own making: once a manufacturer was in our system and recognized to be Red List free, they had little incentive to do more. The value of full public transparency was diminished. Instead of producers of information, we had become consumers. We had to refine our "ask," further sharpen our advocacy, and demand better, even as we settled for good enough.

To manage the process — indeed, to even come to a decision on any given product — we developed an internal order of operations. The priorities, in order, were:

- Health over full transparency
- Health over local sourcing
- Health over embodied carbon

Recognizing carbon's existential threat, some may question the last decision point. Carbon, we concluded, may be offset, while negative health impacts cannot — particularly for any individual who had been affected. That said, increasingly rigid application of this structure helped us arrive at decisions efficiently, but it was not clear that we were making better choices. In many instances, good information was available for one of the facets in question, but not all. We came to realize that we couldn't apply a rigid priority hierarchy to all product types for all projects and clients.

Today, our approach is more flexible and can adapt depending on the product, the manufacturer's degree of transparency, and our client's agenda. Advocacy once again becomes an essential tool, this time to address shortcomings in one or more facets. We can add as many facets as necessary, as long as we have a clear, actionable goal that can be the basis for our advocacy "ask." We expect that mindful MATERIALS' Common Materials Framework will provide a durable guide, but we also anticipate that new criteria will arise, just as Grace Farms has brought embodied injustice into consideration in recent years. While there are generally prescribed requirements that must be met to achieve a specific certification, each client's sustainability agenda is different. One owner might wish to address entire classes of chemicals of concern, rather than specific CAS numbers, while another may have more interest in confronting social justice issues.

Rather than diluting the effort to secure transparency, as might be inferred from this process, varying the focus can help mitigate the pitfalls of single-variable optimization in the pursuit of sustainability. Not long ago, at a conference, we witnessed a presenter electrify an audience of energy efficiency

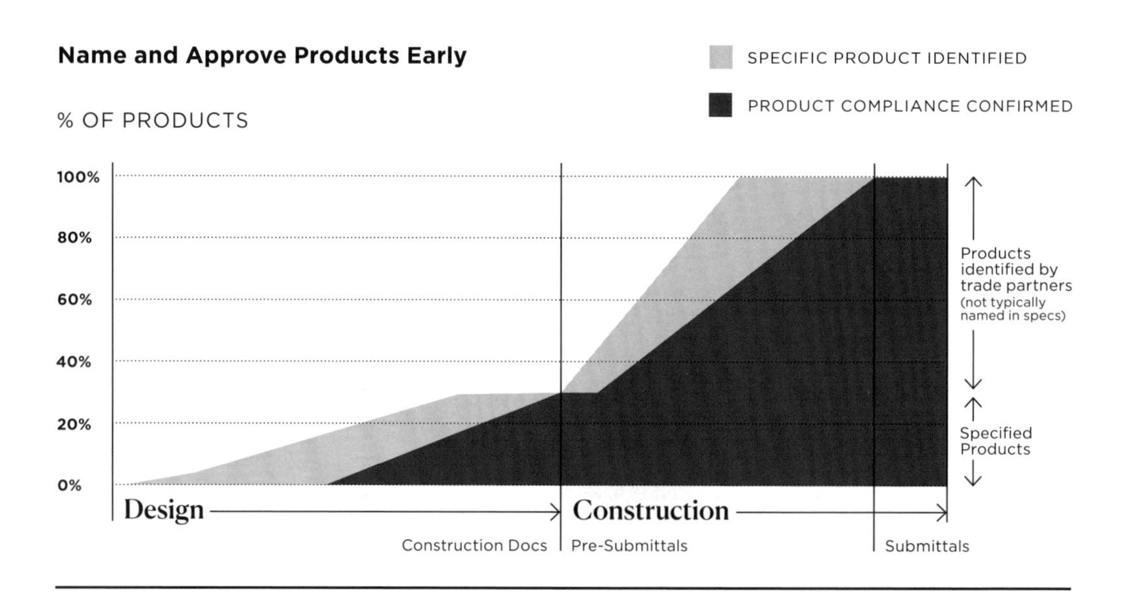

Figure 5. In the Red2Green materials management process, introducing a "Pre-Submittal" requirement for subcontractors helped ensure that virtually every product can be considered by the full project team before approval and use. As a result, trade partners understand at the outset that *all* products, not just those on the spec sheets, warrant examination.

CHASING THE DREAM: TRACKING, MANAGING, AND REUSING SUSTAINABILITY DATA

New buildings, with few exceptions, begin with essentially a clean slate. Owners want fresh and unique; designers oblige. Spec sheets, however, provide the team with "comfort food." Each novel, shiny building is typically underpinned by remarkably conventional materials — products everybody knows, and which perpetuate the status quo. Change requires deft, multifaceted adjustments to the process.

Ideally, this begins with specific healthier materials language in RFPs and by thoughtfully assessing prospective building teams' commitment to sustainability. Reluctant participants will impede efforts, prompting IES to inaugurate team meetings early on to encourage buy-in. A required "Pre-Submittal" lists both specified and unspecified (i.e., not in design documents) materials that subcontractors intend to use. Researchers review Pre-Submittals, identify issues, and provide feedback to the design/construction team — and negotiation ensues. Fundamentally, team members need to know, "Can I use this product on the project?" By answering this question repeatedly, as early as possible, the process remains simple. Complications arise when managing communication and results for hundreds and, presently, tens of thousands of products. Spreadsheets, though commonly used even now, are inadequate for understanding and documenting such a project, let alone providing usable intelligence for ensuing projects or across a portfolio.

Advances in finding and using healthier materials might have largely plateaued without the advent of Red2Green (R2G), IES' materials management platform, and the strategies it supports. Launched in 2015 to assist healthier materials research, R2G began as a data repository that also guided researchers. Tabbed pages, each featuring a discrete aspect — ingredients, sourcing, manufacturer information, documentation — efficiently ushered users step-by-step through researching, evaluating and advocating for any product type.

Working side by side, researchers and developers swiftly expanded platform capabilities. Materials specialists requesting new features often had them by week's end, sometimes the following day. The diverse team, talented but new to healthy materials research, created a sophisticated tool featuring real-time team communication, API-linked product information, materials tracking, manufacturing outreach and advocacy templates, and a Portfolio View ensuring project-to-project continuity. Perhaps most significantly, R2G today allows for continual addition of materials research facets as new concerns emerge, enabling users to compare and evaluate vital considerations such as embodied carbon and social justice.

History gives us a clear indication of the future. Materials goals will push us to include more, not fewer, facets of their impact and benefit. As we contemplate these new facets, data will at first be spotty and suspect, but over time will grow in quantity and quality. Advocacy will fuel this growth.

professionals. Their presentation on the ingredients concerns raised by the selection and use of energy-conserving building materials and products immediately became the gathering's hottest topic. Participants realized that by concentrating primarily on straightforward methods such as insulation, sealing and cutting-edge efficiency, they had failed to adequately consider the environmental effects of products used to accomplish energy goals. The lessons of that day continue to resonate.

The same applies to product types. Wood products engender different concerns than paints and coatings, which in turn present different issues than wiring and electronic devices. One manufacturer may be asked to seek FSC certification, another to evaluate VOCs, and a third to change insulation or pursue the Restriction of Hazardous Substances Directive, or RoHS. This need for targeted efforts led us to develop and refine concise, easily versioned advocacy outreach templates, which were added to the materials management program and made readily available to the research team.

History gives us a clear indication of the future. Materials goals will push us to include more, not fewer, facets of their impact and benefit. As we contemplate these new facets, data will at first be spotty and suspect, but over time will grow in quantity and quality. Advocacy will fuel this growth. Rather than responding to one-off requests from project teams, manufacturers will support a dominant standard; they will also publish their information electronically to maximize their reach and minimize their costs. Project teams will plug into a web of data, but they will need a way to evaluate what constitutes "good enough" at a given moment, as well as the means to track their own decisions over time.

Judging by our recent projects, this healthier materials work is about 20 percent complete, but those successes are concentrated in high visibility product categories, such as carpet tile, interior paint, and acoustical ceilings. As we factor in other considerations, we are realistically only about 5 percent toward the finish line. Social justice considerations, for example, are clearly important, but the process of defining disclosure practices, criteria, and thresholds is still very much in development. No matter what facets are considered, the rules should be the same: find a good enough product, one that we feel comfortable using, but do so while joining our voices to advocate for its improvement. These small efforts, amplified through repetition and tracked through time, will advance us to the regenerative and considerate future market that we all seek.

Charley Stevenson, LFA, LEED AP is Integrated Eco Strategy (IES) Consulting Principal and CEO of Red2Green Materials Management Software. Charley Stevenson's interest in sustainable design began in the early 1990s when he graduated from Williams College with a concentration in Environmental Studies. He received his MS in Natural Science from Rensselaer Polytechnic Institute in 2002. Since then, he has worked on sustainable projects in a variety of capacities and, as a volunteer, has been active in a range of land conservation and renewable energy projects.

In 2008, Stevenson joined a consulting engineering firm specializing in energy modeling and sustainability certification. Two years later he founded IES, where he soon focused on helping clients meet the demanding, industry-changing Living Building Challenge standards. His company has now managed the green aspects of institutional projects ranging from 1,000 to 500,000 square feet.

Charley's work in regenerative design is rooted in his passion for teaching. A former high school math and science teacher, Charley is vice chair of the Burr and Burton Academy, Manchester, VT, board. He is a member of the ILFI Material Health technical advisory group and a frequent presenter at Living Future and other sustainability conferences.

INTEGRATED ECO STRATEGY

Located in North Adams, MA, IES has provided sustainability support for more than seventy projects including the Harvard University Science and Engineering Complex, Williams College Environmental Center, Hampshire College Kern Center, Stanley Center for Peace and Security, The Ecology School and the Yale Divinity School Regenerative Village. IES' affiliate, Red2Green Management Software, is a materials platform used by teams nationwide to facilitate and manage healthier materials selection. The company's 21-member team includes sustainability analysts, healthy materials specialists, researchers and others dedicated to environmental leadership.

Information is available at materiallybetter.com.

Photo: Joel Jasmin Forestbird/Unsplash

Conclusion

Building a Future: What Good Looks Like

Alison Mears

&

Jonsara Ruth

Imagine a built world created with the intention of supporting people's health, nature's ecologies, environments, and all living things.

What if homes made people healthier? What if building materials and their production processes sequestered carbon from the atmosphere? What if these materials were made primarily from plants that naturally biodegrade? And what if the demand for these materials increased the need for healthy agricultural processes and created new jobs for rural agrarian and other forgotten communities? What if we used agricultural byproducts to make new materials using innovative, low-energy technologies?

If we take lessons from ancient Indigenous cultures that have lived in harmony with

Wild Rice Growing on Shell Lake, White Earth Reservation, Minnesota, 2019.

nature for thousands of years, our future will be regenerative. Indigenous wisdom asks us to nurture the planet's abundant resources to support human life for the next generations. Our livelihoods, our lives, children and future generations are our joint responsibility. Clean water, clean energy, fertile soils, and healthy, affordable houses for everyone are possible only through reconsidering and regenerating our human activities. What if all of today's decision makers prioritized people's health, nature's ecosystems, and all living things?

We live in a time when our human actions have overtaken the natural cycles of our planet's ecosystem. Humanity is confronting multiple interconnected ecosystem challenges that are accelerating because of the climate crisis. As designers and builders, as owners and residents, we must address this issue as we center people and the planet. The problems of carbon emissions and toxic chemicals are inextricably linked.

Refined fossil fuels are both massive carbon emitters and the source of ingredients for products that pollute neighborhoods and homes. The rate of plastics used in residential housing has exponentially increased. Plastics are used in practically every part of a conventional building and are part of the unregulated supply chain of toxic ingredients used in building products. Materials that are used to make buildings, cities, objects, and furniture are literally becoming part of our biological systems as they are absorbed by the oceans, our waterways, and even our bodies and those of other living creatures. Yet, most people are not aware of this problem.

The challenge is that so many significant impacts from the building industry are invisible. A shiny new floor doesn't reveal the number of children suffering from asthma precisely because they live near the factory that made that flooring material. The beautiful paint color on a wall doesn't evidence the enormous amount of microplastics in the ocean that are a result of its production and use. Inexpensive polyvinyl chloride (PVC) plumbing, furniture, flooring, and other vinyl materials do not illuminate the cost of rising infertility rates, lowering sperm counts, and the growing industry of high-tech interventions and medicines intended support successful pregnancies and future families.

How do we change from where we are now to where we want to be? When will we adopt innovative policies that confront an uncertain future and benefit all people and the planet? We live in a time when impacts of decisions made by our predecessors are irrefutable. A change in mindset is necessary — a unified acknowledgment that we must shift from how things have been done for the last century to another way, where the

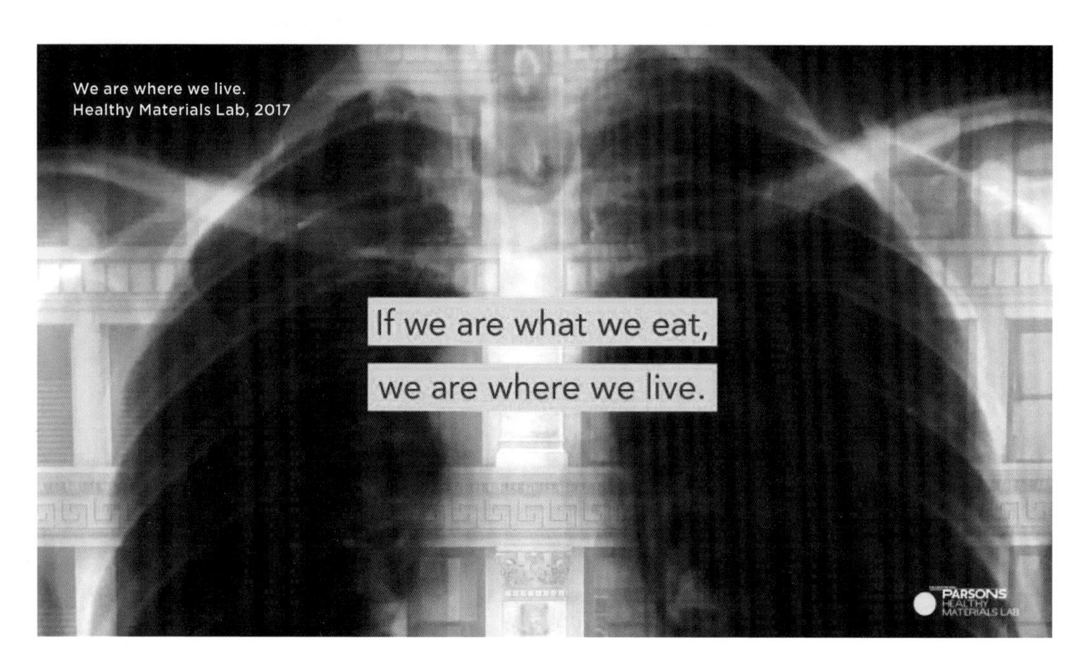

We are where we live.
Healthy Materials Lab, 2017

health of people and ecosystems is primary in every decision. Mapping the way forward is the responsibility of all of us. We all work to change the practice of architecture and design and work towards the construction of healthier buildings. We look to governments to implement new climate/toxic reduction policies to guide and scale the systemic change needed to overturn the negative global warming impacts of building and transition cities towards a more sustainable future. Ideally, we need policies that protect people from exposure to toxics and other hazards and reduce the negative impact of carbon emissions from buildings and in cities. Such policies are beginning to take shape.

Since 2016, several key policy initiatives have responded to the climate crisis and the need to reduce carbon emissions: the Paris Agreement, the UN Sustainability Goals, European Green Deal, and in the United States, the Green New Deal. If fully adopted, these initiatives and programs have the potential to evoke meaningful change on a global scale. New carbon and materials policies are being implemented in the European Union (EU) and Nordic countries where Environmental Product Declarations will be required for all products. Some countries — Denmark, for example — are going even further by setting annual targets for embodied carbon.

Green building programs can drive change when legislation lags. In the United States, for example, Enterprise Green Communities Criteria (EGCC) is the only national green building program created for the affordable housing sector to advance racial equity and achieve economic and environmental justice. The criteria provide cost-effective standards for creating healthy and energy-efficient homes. Thirty US states require or encourage developers seeking affordable housing funding to conform to EGCC best practices for design and construction. Legislation is a major incentive to build healthier housing.

There are numerous efforts to reduce the number of harmful chemicals in the products used to make our homes and buildings, and to reduce the embodied carbon in our materials and buildings. But what if materials and buildings were constructed to promote health for all people, environments, and communities today, instead of incrementally doing less harm? We can build a new future by designing nature-based practices; creating viable, marketable products; integrating and transforming existing structures; supporting resilient and regenerative systems; and building healthy, affordable places for everyone. We can reconsider the places

We can build a new future by designing nature-based practices; creating viable, marketable products; integrating and transforming existing structures; supporting resilient and regenerative systems; and building healthy, affordable places for everyone.

Hemplime Insulation Installed at PA Hemp Home, Pennsylvania, 2021.

where we live as Adrian McGregor describes them: "biocities... spectacular living, dynamic systems that (can) evolve with us" (Wright, 2023).

A vision for a better future is vivid thanks to the work of many people, many of whose voices are shared in this book. All of us are invested in a future where our health, in the largest definition — societal, urban, economic, political, environmental, and human — will thrive. Material health is part of a coordinated effort to address all of the negative impacts of human processes on the planet. We begin with the idea of regenerative practices where justice and equity, climate and biodiversity, and humanity are interconnected with the aim of eliminating the climate crisis. By focusing on regenerative materials in our buildings, we can return to the bountiful potential of our planet. We can be responsible stewards of the land. We can ensure that we consider the lives of generations to come and leave the world a better place than we found it.

A healthy relationship between the natural world and humanity is fundamental to sustaining and supporting human life. It is time to reject the historic and extractive dualities that have existed in Western culture — between nature and culture; between mind and body — because such thinking isolates us from the very essence of what makes us human and disconnects us from all other species. The knowledge that

Industrial Hemp Field, Kentucky, 2019.

exists within indigenous communities and in the Global South provides us with important materials systems guidance. The natural world extends to all environments and all species, always providing opportunities to reimagine the way we create and build and inhabit space. Fundamentally we need to acknowledge the interconnectedness of us all.

And while the planet will continue to evolve and remain in existence without us, we humans depend on our interdependent relationships with natural systems for our long-term survival, and to thrive. We must regain our ability to live in harmony with the planet rather than at odds with it. We can harness our innate ability to innovate, invent and recover a better way of living and building. As architects and designers, we are uniquely positioned to make changes to our practice that can have profound benefits to our own lives and the planet. By tackling and removing toxics from building products, reducing embodied carbon, and rethinking the design of the cities that house buildings, we can revolutionize our relationships with the environment. We can make healthier places with healthy, regenerative materials that cultivate equitable labor practices. It's already happening. We now need to shift to exponentially and radically scaling this progress.

The late Robin Guenther, a pioneer in the material health movement and principal architect at Perkins and Will, famously said: *"There are only two choices: we either believe we create the future through every decision we make, or we believe the future is determined and our job is simply to keep on the path. I'm dedicated to the first choice."*

A new innovative path for decision making is possible. We need positive, radical collaboration at scale, and the built world will evolve into one that is regenerative, just, healthy, and prosperous for many generations to come. This change is imperative, and the time is NOW.

REFERENCES

Wright, Keira. (2023, May 20). ***Why Thinking of Cities as Nature Is Key to Fighting Climate Change.*** Bloomberg. www.bloomberg.com/news/articles/2023-05-30/biourbanism-why-thinking-of-cities-as-nature-is-key-to-fighting-climate-change

HEALTHY MATERIALS LAB

Healthy Materials Lab (HML) at Parsons School of Design was established in 2015 in direct response to the complex, intertwined issues threatening our culture, our planet, and the health of our families. Specifically, we focus on the myriad issues surrounding building materials and their impact on human health and the environment. With the knowledge that design, architecture, and construction contribute to many of our global problems, HML finds ways for these professions to be part of the solution.

HML is a design research lab focused on improving the quality of the built environment through the use of materials and building products so that all people may live healthier lives. Together with partners, Healthy Building Network, Green Science Policy Institute, and Health Product Declaration Collaborative, they are supported by a grant from The JPB Foundation specifically to transform affordable housing to be healthier.

Their objective is to provide resources to architects and designers so that they, too, can put human health and environmental health at the center of all design decisions. They do this by creating education (courses, lectures, events, podcasts) and resources (healthy materials collections, healthy building guidelines, design method cards, case studies) for designers and architects, and other professionals who build homes. Each year they engage in collaborations with community development organizations to demonstrate how healthier homes can be built. Metropolis magazine recently featured the lab, stating, "Healthy Materials Lab is redefining sustainable design". (here is a link). Their new book, Material Health: Design Frontiers, published in 2023, and edited by Ruth and Mears, brings together experts from a wide range of disciplines to describe and define the new field of material health.

Alison Mears and Jonsara Ruth co-founded Healthy Materials Lab at Parsons in 2015. The design research team is made up of faculty, full-time and postgraduate researchers, graduate and undergraduate student researchers, and a committee of expert advisors from a wide variety of fields, including design, architecture, environmental justice, circular economy, public health, material engineering, climate specialists and design theory. They employ an interdisciplinary, collaborative approach to solving problems. In 2022, Alison Mears and Jonsara Ruth were awarded the "Women in Architecture Innovation Award" from Architectural Record.

Alison Mears As co-founder and Director of the Healthy Materials Lab, Alison leverages her practice-based experience as an architect and her knowledge and experience as a long-term academic leader to confront one of the more serious and often overlooked environmental challenges of our time: the health of the built environment. How do we make profound and long-term changes to everyday design practice to create truly healthy buildings, especially for those in the most need in affordable housing? HML creates resources, educational programming, and prototypical innovative housing models for a new post petroleum world. Alison is co-Principal Investigator of the Healthy Affordable Materials Project (HAMP). The Project is a long-term coalition of four organizations that work together to remove harmful chemicals from the built environment. She is also the recipient of multiple grants that support the work of the Lab.

Alison's work draws from the long tradition at The New School University's commitment to promoting community-based sustainability, social engagement, and environmental justice, especially in her teaching in architectural design studios at Parsons. She lectures widely, disseminating current thinking within the field of material health.

Jonsara Ruth is driven by a curiosity for materials, seeking to elevate human experience through design. She is co-founder and Design Director of Healthy Materials Lab (HML) at Parsons School of Design, where she is an Associate Professor and Founding Director of the MFA Interior Design program. At HML, Jonsara co-leads a team of dedicated researchers to imagine ways to design healthier, sustainable futures with the ambitious goal of improving the health of underserved communities through the transformation of design and material practices.

Drawing from over a decade as a designer in the furniture industry, Jonsara brings her understanding of manufacturing, supply chains, labor practices, and a penchant for democratic design to her roles at HML and Parsons. She draws from her artistic practice to creatively lead, motivate change and inspire new methods for making and imagining futures.

She founded Salty Labs, a design collective, to experiment and implement ideas of circularity while utilizing healthy, low-carbon materials and strategies, working closely with local artisans to design interiors, furniture, and experiences. Jonsara's work can be seen internationally in numerous publications, exhibitions, and people's homes. She frequently contributes as a lecturer, critic, guest expert, and advisor to design institutions, media, and publications, currently serving on the board of advisors for the Sustainable Furnishings Council. Jonsara's lifelong creative goal is to serve society and culture through her work.

Best Practices for Red List Free Affordable Housing

Susan Puri

Hannah Ray

&

Kathleen Smith

ACKNOWLEDGEMENTS TO THE FOLLOWING REVIEWERS:

Leila Behjat, Senior Design Researcher, Parsons School of Design

Lisa Carey Moore, Director of Buildings, International Living Future Institute

Michael Kloefkorn, Principal, Van Meter Williams Pollack Architecture

Gladys Ly-Au Young, Founding Partner, Sundberg Kennedy Ly-Au Young Architects

Alison Mears, Director and Co-Founder, Healthy Materials Lab, Parsons School of Design

Adam Meier, Director of Green and Healthy Communities, Housing Partnership Network

Mona Nahm, Designer, Y.A. Studio

Erika Schreder, Science Director, Toxic Free Future

Veena Singla, Ph.D, Senior Scientist, Natural Resources Defense Council

Roberto Valle Kinloch, Ph.D, HomeFree Manager, Healthy Building Network

This resource with live links is available as a free download at **living-future.org/affordable-housing-guidebook**

The International Living Future Institute (ILFI or the Institute) envisions a future where all materials in the built environment have positive impacts on human, community, and ecosystem health. All ingredients within building products would be fully disclosed and free of toxicants and harmful chemicals.

With this vision, ILFI created the Red List to identify the "worst -in-class" substances prevalent in the building industry that pose serious risks to human health and the environment. We have been working with affordable housing project teams and partners since 2011 to eliminate the use of Red List chemicals in affordable housing. Over the last three years, the Institute has created the Affordable Housing Materials List, which is a downloadable spreadsheet of products, by CSI division, that can be used, along with Declare, to help simplify the process of creating Red List Free

Block Project, Seattle, WA. Image Courtesy of Facing Homelessness.

specifications for affordable housing and other project types. Declare is an easy-to-read 'nutrition label' for products with online resources to promote, share, and find healthier building materials. The creation of the Affordable Housing Materials List and research by many teams have helped inform this guide.

It can be daunting to approach an overhaul of standard specifications or to design a Red List Free building, particularly for an affordable housing project team that more than likely has budget and time constraints, as well as a need to keep maintenance costs low. Material health information listing chemical names can be intimidating to engage with for a building professional who is, by training, not a toxicology expert and likely does not have advanced degrees in chemistry. It can be tempting to assume that there are regulations in place to protect from harmful chemicals in products; however, this is unfortunately not the case. There is no legal requirement for manufacturers of building materials to publish their ingredients and very limited regulation around chemicals in products.[1] It will take a collective effort by those in the affordable housing sector and in the healthy materials realm to ensure that materials for affordable housing are safe and affordable. This guide will help identify which Red List ingredients are common in each product category, the health implications of including Red List ingredients, and, most importantly, the alternatives and best categories to start with to move towards Red List Free affordable housing.

This guide is intended to provide information for architects, designers, consultants, contractors, owners, developers, maintenance and facility staff, and others seeking to make healthier material choices for their residents, workers, and communities. The outcome we ultimately strive for at ILFI is regenerative and healthy built environments for all people. We also strive to eliminate the effects of Red List chemicals on everyone who interacts with them, including factory workers, installers, occupants of buildings, those involved in end-of-life disposal, and surrounding communities. This is even more critical in Black, Indigenous, People of Color (BIPOC) and low-wealth communities, which have historically suffered and continue to suffer disproportionate exposure to environmental hazards (in the air, water, soil, and buildings) due to unjust and racist policies such as redlining that have resulted in worse health outcomes in these communities.

This guide is primarily focused on health-related attributes, as defined by the Red List. Note that this guidance is not intended as a pathway for achieving the Materials Petal in the Living Building Challenge (LBC) or Core Certifications and does not cover all requirements for these certifications, which are holistic and address a spectrum of issues in the built environment. ILFI has a multi-attribute approach to materials as explained in the sections below and has many other resources available on our website to reference for these attributes (such as embodied carbon[2]). We are creating this guide to invite more organizations in the affordable housing sector to join us on this mission by installing as many Red List Free materials as feasible in each project while simultaneously pushing and signaling to the market a demand for more Red List Free products that are affordable.

THE RED LIST

Since its inception in 2006, the Red List has been an intuitive tool for communicating the need to stop using chemicals that cause harm. The Red List represents the worst-in-class chemicals that are prevalent in the built environment; it does not include every possible hazardous chemical and it should also not be applied to consumer products or sectors where other types of

1 For more information around chemical regulations in the United States, refer to Krimsky S. The unsteady state and inertia of chemical regulation under the US Toxic Substances Control Act. Birnbaum LS, editor. PLoS Biol [Internet]. 2017 Dec 18 [cited 2018 Mar 2];15(12):e2002404. Available from: http://dx.plos.org/10.1371/journal.pbio.2002404

2 Embodied carbon refers to the greenhouse gas emissions arising from the manufacturing, transportation, installation, maintenance, and disposal of building materials. In contrast, operational carbon refers to the greenhouse gas emissions due to building energy consumption.(https://carbonleadershipforum.org/embodied-carbon-101/). Embodied carbon has a significant contribution to climate change, which also disproportionately affects BIPOC and low-income communities, who typically experience more impacts of extreme heat and weather events.

chemicals are more common. As a binary screen to assess material health, the Red List brings simplicity to a complex topic. Once a project team has found product ingredient information, they can easily identify any Red List ingredients by cross checking the Chemical Abstract Service Registry Number (CASRN) identification numbers against the published spreadsheet of CASRN numbers on the Red List. The Red List is central to several of ILFI's programs, including the Materials Petal of the LBC, the Living Product Challenge (LPC), and the Declare Label. Red List compounds must be avoided at the level of 100 ppm, or 0.01% of a product, in LBC projects, Red List Free Declare Labels, and LPC products and process chemicals.

The chemical classes on the Red List range widely in structure, toxicity, and function. They include toxic legacy building materials like asbestos and polychlorinated biphenyls (PCBs) that are now illegal in most applications, but still found in many existing buildings; chemicals that are regulated, but not banned, like formaldehyde and other volatile organic compounds; and compounds of emerging concern that are pervasive in many products like ortho-phthalates, halogenated flame retardants, and per- and polyfluoroalkyl substances (PFAS). The Red List also includes chemical classes that have potential for harm during the extraction, processing, manufacture, or disposal stages of the product life cycle.[3] Red List compounds are found in many building products including drywall, insulation, adhesives, paint and other finishes, lighting fixtures, resilient flooring, waterproofing, textiles, windows, and more.

Each product or ingredient screened for an LBC project or a Declare label creates

THE PATH TO OPTIMIZED PRODUCT HEALTH

The path to optimized product health includes the necessary steps a manufacturer must take toward improving the health profile of their products. This entails making sure the substances and materials within their products do not pose and health impacts to building occupants or those working in or living near the manufacturing plants. The following five steps have been identified by the industry:

1. KNOW
Fully understand a material's ingredients and its production process

2. DISCLOSE
The act of sharing product content and/or its impacts publicy through approved certifications, labels, or standards

3. SCREEN
Using known hazard lists to screen ingredients or processes for potential impacts

4. ASSESS
A more rigorous investigation to determine the health and environmental impacts of each substance or material in the product

5. OPTIMIZE
Removing or replacing chemicals with ones that have less impact on health or the environment

3 This report from Energy Efficiency for All and Healthy Building Network explains the life cycle and environmental justice impacts of certain chemicals of concern.

How Chemicals From Building Materials Enter Our Bodies

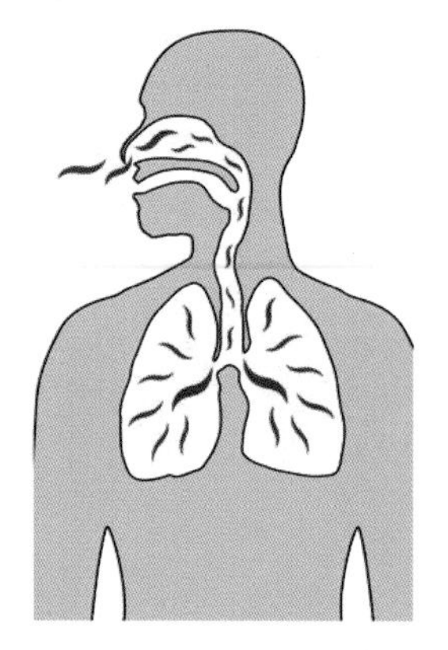

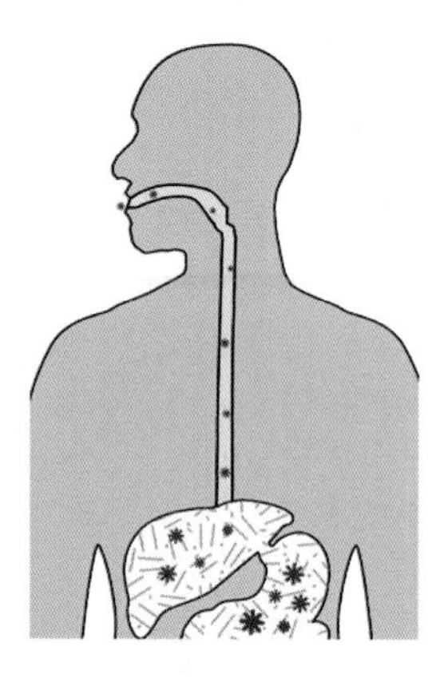

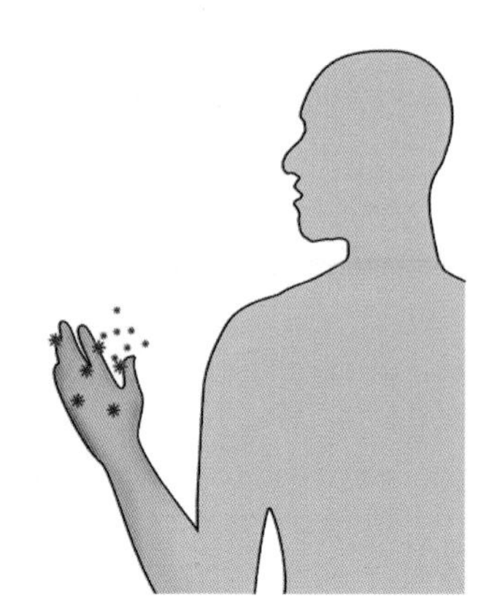

Chemicals from building materials can get into our bodies in three different ways.
Image courtesy of Healthy Materials Lab at Parsons School of Design.

Ingestion:
Direct ingestion of water or dust that has been contaminated by chemicals migrating from building materials.

Inhalation:
Breathing air that has been contaminated by chemicals migrating from building materials.

Dermal contact:
Skin contact with chemicals that are present in air, dust, water, contaminated surfaces, and direct product contact. Chemicals may be absorbed by the skin and enter the bloodstream.

opportunities for education, advocacy, and positive change. Thanks to the efforts of many in the building sector, the avoidance of Red List chemicals has sparked the innovation of new approaches that reduce the use of toxicants in buildings. For example, buildings can be designed with materials that do not require finishes, which often contain chemicals of concern, or without plenum spaces to maximize the use of low-smoke, halogen-free electrical cable. Declare and the broader transparency movement in the industry have pushed manufacturers to innovate and to eliminate Red List chemicals that have been standard in specific applications for many years. Among many others, Declare now includes composite wood products without formaldehyde, a tiling system that does not require mortar or adhesives, and an insulated panel without halogenated flame retardants.

The Red List is updated annually to stay current with science and policy. Early versions of the Red List flagged 13 chemical classes and ~300 individual compounds. As of 2023, the list comprises 19 chemical classes and over 11,000 individual compounds.

HEALTH HAZARDS

The descriptions below include the types of health and environmental hazards that are present in the chemical classes included on the Red List.

Acute aquatic toxicity: Hazardous to aquatic environment and aquatic life.[4]

Acute or chronic organ or system toxicity: Causing damage to organs or organ systems including the liver, kidneys, nervous system, hemoglobin function, and lung tissue.[5]

Antibiotic Resistance: The ability of germs like bacteria or fungi to develop the ability to defeat the drugs designed to kill them, threatening the ability of medical advances to fight infections.

Asthmagen: A substance that can induce or exacerbate symptoms of asthma (shortness of breath, wheezing, coughing, and chest tightness[6]). A 2013 report by Healthy Building Network named twenty of these asthmagens to be of thet highest priority, due to clear pathways for building occupants to be exposed to them after product installation and during normal use. Priority asthmagens identified include: acid aldehydes (two types); acrylates (four types); ammonium hydroxide; bisphenol A diglycidyl ether (BADGE); ethanolamines (three types); formaldehyde; isocyanates (six types); polyfunctional aziridine; and, styrene.[7]

Carcinogen: Any substance or agent that is capable of causing cancer — the abnormal or uncontrolled growth of new cells in any part of the body in humans or animals. Most carcinogens are chronic toxins with long latency periods that can cause damage after repeated or long duration exposures and often do not have immediate apparent harmful effects.[8]

Developmental toxicant: A substance that can cause harm to a developing child, including birth defects, low birth weight, and biological or behavioral problems that appear as the child grows.[9]

Endocrine disruptor: A chemical compound that interferes with the normal functioning of the endocrine system (glands which secrete hormones into the blood) and the reproductive and other biological processes regulated by it.

Immunotoxicant: A substance that causes adverse effects on the functioning of the immune system. Immunotoxicity leads to the increased incidence or severity of infectious diseases or cancer, since the immune system's ability to respond adequately to invading agents is suppressed.[10]

Mutagenic: Anything that causes a mutation (a change in the DNA of a cell). DNA changes caused by mutagens may harm cells and cause certain diseases, such as cancer.

Neurotoxin: A substance that alters the normal activity of the nervous system. This can eventually disrupt or even kill neurons (nerve cells) which are important for transmitting and processing signals in the brain and other parts of the nervous system,[11] causing symptoms such as numbness.

Ozone depleting: Chemicals that degrade ozone layer, the atmospheric shield that protects from high doses of UV radiation, which causes increased incidences of skin cancer and damages plants and marine ecosystems.[12] International action to ban CFCs in the 1980s has resulted in a notable recovery in the ozone layer.[13]

Heavy metals: Cadmium, mercury, lead and other metals that cause health problems including cancer, developmental issues, lung and kidney damage, bone loss, hypertension, breathing problems, anemia, ulcers, and allergic reactions.[14]

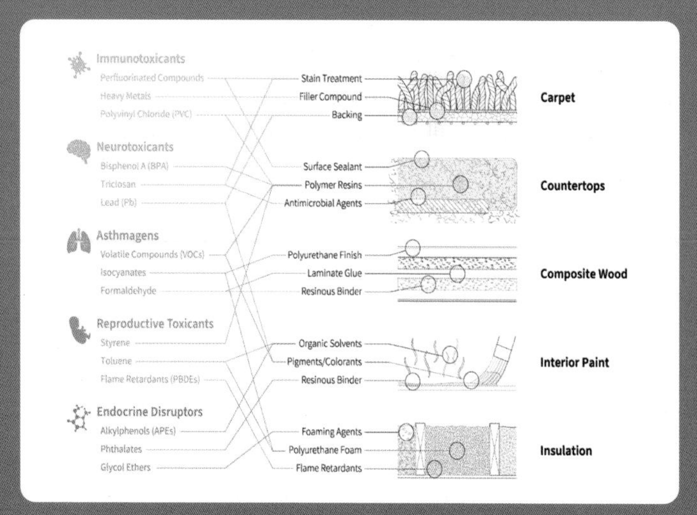

Figure 1: An example of the types of chemicals found on the Red List and where they can be found in the built environment.

Particularly hazardous due to persistence: The trait of chemicals, such as those that fall under the PFAS chemical class, to be extremely resistant to environmental and metabolic degradation, and sometimes, but not always resulting in higher concentrations over time and difficulties in removing contamination.[15] These are often referred to as "forever chemicals."

Persistent Organic Pollutant (POP)/ Persistent Bioaccumulative Toxic (PBT): A set of toxic chemicals that are persistent in the environment and able to last for several years before breaking down. POPs circulate globally and chemicals released in one part of the world can be deposited at far distances from their original source through a repeated process of evaporation and deposition. POPs are lipophilic, which means that they accumulate in the fatty tissue of living animals and human beings. In fatty tissue, the concentrations can become magnified by up to 70,000 times higher than the background levels. As you move up the food chain, concentrations of POPs tend to increase so that animals at the top of the food chain such as fish, predatory birds, mammals, and humans tend to have the greatest concentrations of these chemicals, and therefore are also at the highest risk from acute and chronic toxic effects.[16]

Reproductive Toxicant: A substance or agent that can cause adverse effects on the reproductive system. The toxic effects may include alterations to the reproductive organs and/or to the endocrine system (which includes the thyroid and adrenal glands). These effects can occur in both men and women.[17]

Very persistent, very bioaccumulative (vPvB): Substances of very high concern due to their persistence, accumulation in living organisms, ability to travel long distances, and high toxicity.[18]

4 www.kemi.se/prioguiden/english/start/prio-criteria-for-phase-out-substances-and-priority-risk-reduction-substances
5 enhs.uark.edu/_resources/documents/sops/Specific_Target_Organ_Toxicants_12.19.pdf
6 enhs.uark.edu/_resources/documents/sops/Specific_Target_Organ_Toxicants_12.19.pdf www.hse.gov.uk/foi/internalops/og/og-00016.htm
7 enhs.uark.edu/_resources/documents/sops/Specific_Target_Organ_Toxicants_12.19.pdf healthybuilding.net/uploads/files/gb2014-asthmagen-paper.pdf
8 ehs.cornell.edu/research-safety/chemical-safety/laboratory-safety-manual/chapter-9-particularly-hazardous-6
9 homefree.healthybuilding.net/glossary
10 www.sciencedirect.com/topics/chemistry/immunotoxicity
11 www.ninds.nih.gov/health-information/disorders/neurotoxicity#
12 www.nationalgeographic.com/environment/article/ozone-depletion
13 www.wbur.org/onpoint/2023/01/30/how-the-world-came-together-to-save-the-ozone-layer
14 living-future.org/red-list/
15 www.ncbi.nlm.nih.gov/pmc/articles/PMC7784706/
16 www.unep.org/cep/persistent-organic-pollutants-pops-and-pesticides
17 ehs.cornell.edu/research-safety/chemical-safety/laboratory-safety-manual
18 risctox.istas.net/en/index.asp?idpagina=613

POSITIVE IMPACTS

The Institute's Red List and programs such as Declare, LBC, and the LPC have greatly raised awareness about the importance of material health within the regenerative building community. Diverse stakeholders reference or integrate the Red List in building standards, procurement policies, design strategies, and specifications. Thousands of manufacturers now voluntarily disclose ingredients and screen for the Red List. As our understanding of the health, environmental, and societal impacts of building materials increases in sophistication, the Red List and ILFI's material health programs will need to evolve as well. The material health community is aligning goals and strategies to work collectively toward making material optimization (the substitution of chemicals with health hazards across the product's life cycle) the norm rather than the exception.

INTERNATIONAL LIVING FUTURE INSTITUTE'S APPROACH TO MATERIALS

ILFI's programs promote a positive and holistic vision of what good looks like for materials, emphasizing green chemistry approaches to product development, regenerative rather than extractive feedstocks, innovative approaches to carbon sequestration and waste remediation, and attention to equity in supply chains and other life cycle stages. ILFI has several programs addressing the multiple attributes related to building materials.

Transparency

The first step towards understanding if a product is healthy or not is transparency. In the materials health sphere, the concept of "transparency" or "disclosure" is the notion that manufacturers should be transparent with consumers about the ingredients and chemistry of their products. This is often not a simple request for manufacturers. Building products can have complicated supply chains and manufacturers are often not aware themselves of the chemicals that are included in the product or the risks that they may pose. There is also not an industry-wide agreement about the level of disclosure that is needed to fully identify any hazards; either the level of disclosure (parts per million or billion, e.g.) and the overall percentage of ingredients that should be disclosed. The Declare program was created to provide guidance on both of these questions and provide a credible and easy-to-read source for building practitioners to find material health information.

Advocacy

Hand-in-hand with transparency is the role of the project team to "advocate" for healthier materials. This means reaching out to manufacturers to request disclosure of ingredients as well as letting them know that you are specifying (or not specifying) their product based on its material health properties. Even if you are unable to find a Red List Free product for a specific application, actions like this taken by many different project teams signals a demand to manufacturers for healthier products.

Declare

ILFI's Declare label is a "nutrition label" for building products and is the easiest way to quickly find Red List Free products. All active Declare labels are accessible on a free and searchable database. Declare labels disclose all intentionally-added ingredients and residuals at or above 100 ppm (0.01%) present in the final product by weight. Each ingredient must be reported with a chemical name, Chemical Abstract Service Registry Number (CASRN), and percentage or percentage range that is included in the product. These labels report all product ingredients and use a simple color code system to flag chemicals of concern that are on the Red List (in red) or on the Watch List (in orange), which means they may be added to the Red List pending further research. Additional information is provided on the product's final assembly locations, life expectancy, end-of-life options, and overall compliance with relevant requirements of the Living Building Challenge. The Declare database also has filters that can identify products to help project teams achieve points under Enterprise Green Communities and LEED v4.1 and 4.2.

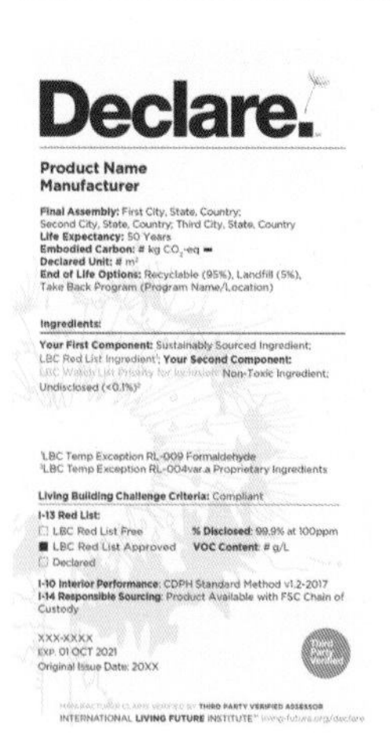

RED LIST FREE products disclose 100% of ingredients present at or above 100 ppm (0.01%) in the final product and do not contain any Red List chemicals.

RED LIST APPROVED products disclose a minimum of 99% of ingredients present in the final product and meet the LBC Red List Imperative requirements through one or more approved exceptions.

DECLARED products disclose 100% of ingredients present in the final product, but contain one or more Red List chemicals that are not covered by an approved exception.

The Living Product Challenge (LPC) is a science-based certification for products that help restore our planet and improve the quality of human life. LPC goes beyond the Red List; not only does it require full disclosure and Red List screen of all ingredients and process chemicals, it also requires full chemical hazard assessment for all ingredients and optimization by removing all ingredients classified as carcinogenic, mutagenic, and/or reprotoxic (CMR), or persistent, bioaccumulative, and toxic (PBT). It encourages the creation of products that give more than they take and assess the entire life cycle impacts in every aspect of the product and its manufacturing process, from fair labor practices in supply chains to material health optimization, energy consumption, water use, impact on communities, and more. LPC products exemplify the

While the Red List is a central element of the Living Building Challenge (LBC), it addresses materials holistically, including the transparency of materials information (through Declare labels), material health (with the Red List), local sourcing, indoor air quality, environmentally responsible sourcing

RED LIST VETTING

This chapter provides an overview of the key steps a project team can use to identify whether a product includes Red List chemicals. The steps below walk through the process for vetting a product for Red List chemicals. There are two basic pathways. The first pathway, Path One, is to use products that have Declare labels products. This pathway is by far the easiest because all products with Declare labels and a Red List Free or Red List Approved Status have already shown they meet the requirements. No additional resaeaching or vetting is required. The second pathway, Path Two, requires research and analysis to determine if a product includes Red List ingredients and, if so, whether it is eligible for an exception within the Living Buidling Challenge. These steps are only comprehensive of the Red List process itself. Additional information and steps will be required for LBC project teams pursuing the full Materials Petal (see the Building Product Selection Guidance on our website for information on holistic materials selection).
Before beginning the vetting process using Path One or Path Two, it is helpful to establish a clear process that everyone on the team understands and commits to. You can use the Pre-Vetting Checklist on the following page to set up this process.

Path One

SELECT

Use products on Declare or on the Affordable Housing Materials List!

If the product has a Declare label, Red List ingredient information is quickly confirmed on the label as:

- **Red List Free:** No Red List chemicals!
- **Red List Approved:** May contain Red List chemicals that are considered unavoidable in the application at this time or may not have fully disclosed all ingredients (though it is confirmed that any withheld are Red List Free). While teams should prioritize Red List Free products, Red List Approved products may be the best in class in certain applications and will help avoid most, even if not all, Red List ingredients.
- **Declared:** Labels that indicate a status of "Declared" contain Red List ingredients. Red List Free or Approved products should be prioritized; however, manufacturers that have taken the first step of transparency should also be commended and these products should be selected over products with no transparent ingredient information.

↓

DO

- **Inform the Manufacturer** with the Declare labeled product that that you chose the product for this reason — this helps the manufacturer to understand continued demand and a return on their investment.
- **Specify the Product.** List the specific Red List Free product in the specifications or performance requirements (such as "Red List Free or Approved") in relevant sections of the project specifications.

Path Two

RESEARCH + REQUEST

If a product has no Declare label, search and/or request ingredient disclosures

- Some manufacturers include information about their product composition on their website. Look for documentation called Health Product Declarations or LBC or LEED letters. You can also use labeled building material repositories, like MindfulMaterials, Ecomedes, UL Spot, and the Health Product Declaration Collaborative to speed your work. Safety Data Sheets (SDS) may list ingredients, but they typically aren't sufficient because they don't require manufacturers to list all ingredients. Manufacturers who have labeled products listed in Declare or other repositories that provide complete health information shouldn't be asked for the information on those labels because they've already done the work. Be respectful of their time.
- If no information is readily available, reach out to the manufacturer. You can download sample "ask" letters from ILFI's Affordable Housing Website.

CONFIRM COMPLIANCE

Confirm Red List Compliance

- Does the product contain Red List ingredients? Cross check all CASRNs against the CASRNs on the Red List and Watch List CASRN Guide. Don't forget to review component ingredients such as a coating used on a product that might not be included in simple material breakdowns (and may be likely to contain Red List ingredients). Note that chemicals on the Watch List are being considered for addition to the Red List, but are not yet included, and those designated as "Priority" are intended to be added to a future version.
- Note that the LBC requires disclosures at 100 ppm (which is more granular than 1,000 or 10,000 ppm). Project teams are encouraged to prioritize products with disclosures at this level, but should choose to use a product disclosed at a lower threshold over a product with no transparency.
- If a product does include Red List ingredients, check if it is covered by an Exception listed in the Living Building Challenge Materials Petal Handbook, as certain chemical classes are unavoidable in particular application (at this time). However, Exceptions are rare and will never apply to cases where there are plenty of Red List Free options (such as resilient flooring).

Confirm VOC Content Compliance — this is part of the Red List scope!

- Is the product an adhesive, coating, or sealant that is wet-applied on site?
- VOCs must be compliant with the limit for that category set by SCAQMD Rule 1168 or CARB 2007 SCM for Architectural Coatings.

If product is Red List Free or Approved

- **Inform the Manufacturer.** Be sure to let a manufacturer with a Red List Free product know that you chose the product for this reason — this helps the manufacturer to understand continued demand and a return on their investment. Suggest they get a Declare Label for this product to make it easier for other project teams to find and specify their product.
- **Specify the Product.** List the specific Red List Free product in the specifications or performance requirements (such as "Red List Free or Approved") in relevant sections.

If product is NOT Red List Free or Approved

- **Begin the process again** on an alternative product and advocate to the manufacturer to provide transparent product information and/or reformulate the product to be Red List Free. Let them know your team is prioritizing healthy materials in your product specifications.

Pre-Vetting Checklist

Before beginning the material vetting process, ensure that you have set up a clear process:

- ☐ **Start early in design**, when you have the flexibility to change or eliminate material selections based on your goals and desired outcomes.
- ☐ **Set a goal.** Even if your project is not pursuing Living Building Challenge certification, having a clear goal in mind for materials (see Chapter 4 for examples of goals) as part of the Owner's Project Requirements (OPR) and Basis of Design (BOD) will provide accountability. Include verified Red List Free products in the BOD specifications to formalize the intent to include them in the final specifications.
- ☐ **Have a clear process for considering material attributes.** Who will lead the effort? What parties are responsible for what building material choices? What tracking and reporting tools will you use to catalog your work and share it among team members? As part of your materials research toolkit, have introductory emails or presentations (for meetings with contractors and other team members), forms that manufacturers can fill out if they don't have a label, and advocacy templates ready to send that ask the manufacturer to address any shortcomings. You can download sample resources from the Institute's Affordable Housing Website and LBC Resources page.
- ☐ **Always keep the "Why?" in mind!** Have a pitch (whether verbal or in writing) ready for project partners (such as manufacturer's representatives and consultants) that includes the information they'll need to be effective partners in the materials research. You can review information about health risks associated with the Red List on our website (or send them an excerpt from this guidebook!). Articles from Trim Tab, such as "Let's Get Down To Business: The Economic Case For Declare And The Living Product Challenge" or "Closing The Transparency Loop: How Building Material Manufacturers Are Transforming The Industry Through Cross-Sector Collaboration,"and even other manufacturer's sites, can help explain how leading manufacturers are embracing transparency and materials health.

Trade workers may be suprised to hear that one benefit of vetting for Red List Chemicals is to eliminate chemicals that can harm them during the installation process because these are not adequately regulated in building materials.

Non-profit and mission-driven affordable housing organizations may want to remember that the production and transport of Red List materials (such as PVC-based products) often release toxic emissions into the air and water[19], which most impacts low-income frontline communities, often the same communities that affordable housing developers are trying to serve.

19 toxicfreefuture.org/research/pvc-poison-plastic/Senathirajah K, Kemp A, Saaristo M, Ishizuka S, Palanisami T. Polymer prioritization framework: A novel multi-criteria framework for source mapping and characterizing the environmental risk of plastic polymers. J Hazard Mater [Internet]. 2022;429(December 2021):128330. Available from: doi.org/10.1016/j.jhazmat.2022.128330

Gila River Indian Community Sustainable Housing, Sacaton, AZ
Photo: courtesy of Wanda Dalla Costa, Arizona State University

PRODUCT GUIDANCE

Armed with some background knowledge, it will now be possible to start to select better products. There are six categories listed below ranking products based on their ingredient content:

1. **Typically Red List Free**
2. **Easy to Spec Red List Free**
3. **Red List free with some cost implication**
4. **Limited options with cost implication**
5. **Few options/request transparency**
6. **Eliminate**

These levels have been informed by ILFI's Affordable Housing Materials List, which is a spreadsheet of products, organized by CSI division, of Red List Free and Approved products found in the Declare and other databases and/or researched by ILFI and our affordable housing project teams. For each level below, project teams may refer to the Affordable Housing Materials List to find specific products.

The guidance included here includes the most common product types that are used by affordable housing project teams and researched by ILFI.. Though not exhaustive it should be comprehensive of the primary types of products for most projects. This guide includes products in CSI Divisions 03 -10, 12, 14, 22, and 26.

Any products not included here or in the Affordable Housing Materials List should be assumed to contain Red List chemicals and should be researched via the Declare database, direct outreach to the manufacturer of the product, and/or through one of the resources included in the Appendix and in Chapter II. Note that some of the products included in this guide may not have Red List chemicals, but may have high embodied carbon, or may not be sourced ethically, or in an environmentally responsible manner. For example, Grace Farms Foundation classifies brick products as a high-risk product for forced labor[1]. It is important to look at product selection holistically and consider multiple attributes in concert[2].

1 Refer to ***Grace Farms Design for Freedom Toolkit*** for information on sourcing masonry and other materials to avoid ethical concerns in the supply chain

2 Refer to ILFI's ***Building Product Selection Guidance*** for a comprehensive guide to selecting materials based on multiple environmental and social attributes.

1. Typically Red List Free

Most of the products included in this section are made of few components. If additional sealers, adhesives, paints, or coatings are added to the material then Red List chemicals may be introduced.

This level includes products under CSI Divisions 03 - 07 and 09.

Division 03 00 00 Concrete

Concrete should not contain any Red List ingredients and can be a good option for flooring or other applications.. The Living Homes at Mill Creek project team used concrete countertops to save on costs and to avoid the Red List ingredients that can be common in several types of countertops. However, sealers, densifiers, and coatings may contain per- and polyfluoroalkyl substances (PFAS), a chemical class on the Red List that has been linked to weakened immune systems, cancer, liver damage, and other health impacts.[3] There are several Red List Free concrete coating products available in Declare. Concrete and cementitious products can contribute significantly to the embodied carbon of a project; project teams are encouraged to select low embodied carbon concrete mixes.[4]

Division 04 00 00 Masonry

Masonry will also not generally contain any Red List chemicals, but project teams will need to avoid using epoxy grouts, which will often contain bisphenol A (BPA)[5], an endocrine disruptor that can affect neurological function and development[6]). Red List Free mortar and grout can be found in Declare.

Division 05 00 00 Metals

05 10 00 Structural Steel
05 40 00 Metal Framing
05 52 00 Metal Railing
05 30 00 Metal Decking
05 51 00 Metal Stairs
05 59 13 Metal Balconies

Also relevant to metals in these sections:

07 60 00 Flashing + Sheet Metal
10 71 00 Exterior Sun Control Devices

Uncoated metals do not generally pose a Red List concern and can be a good option to avoid Red List chemicals. Metal doors for example may be a better option for avoiding Red List chemicals than composite wood doors, which are likely to include formaldehyde. However, some metal coatings and sealers may contain multiple Red List ingredients, such as PFAS or phthalates, they can also be made with or contain hexavalent chromium (a toxic heavy metal that is linked to breathing problems and cancers in factory workers[7]). Many coating products contain Polyvinylidene fluoride (PVDF), which is classified as a PFAS compound. There are Red List Free metal coatings and primers with Declare labels available. Many manufacturers can provide a Galvalume finish, which can be made Red List Free, and should not cost more than other coatings. Steel will also contribute significantly to the embodied carbon of a project.

3 living-future.org/red-list/

4 carbonleadershipforum.org/low-carbon-concrete-implementation-strategy/

5 informed.healthybuilding.net/explore#

6 living-future.org/red-list/

7 living-future.org/red-list/

Division 06 00 00 Wood, Plastics, and Composites

Solid Wood Members

06 10 00 Rough Carpentry
06 30 00 Exterior Carpentry
06 11 00 Wood Framing
06 41 00 Architectural Wood Casework

Also relevant to these sections:

09 64 00 Wood Flooring, including cork and bamboo
12 30 00 Casework
12 36 00 Countertops

Untreated solid wood members used in millwork, wood framing, and wood siding will not contain Red List chemicals. Select solid wood components over composite wood to avoid Red List ingredients (especially formaldehyde, a known carcinogen and asthmagen.) Leave products unfinished and/or select any paints, sealers, coatings, or adhesives without Red List chemicals. Note that there are several Red List Free wood stain and varnish products available in Declare. Utilizing wood products from sustainably managed forests can be a way to decrease the embodied carbon of the project by avoiding concrete or steel in structural members. Wood products (such as wood flooring or siding or base boards) can also be a substitute for plastic products that contain Red List ingredients and pose risks for environmental and human health. Project teams pursuing LBC certification have additional sustainable sourcing requirements for wood products; other project teams are encouraged to prioritize sourcing FSC certified or salvaged wood products in order to avoid detrimental environmental effects associated with deforestation. Wood can be used as a means of bringing biophilic design and a connection to the natural environment into a building, particularly in urban contexts.

Division 07 00 00 Thermal and Moisture Protection

07 21 00 Hempcrete Insulation
07 21 00 Strawbale Insulation
07 21 06 Blown-In Cellulose Insulation

Natural insulating materials, such as strawbale insulation, can be an effective way to eliminate Red List chemicals and decrease the carbon impacts of the building. In appropriate contexts, strawbale or hempcrete can provide sufficient R-value and can be an affordable alternative to conventional insulation[8]. Hemplime insulation has been approved for use as an insulation in the new International Residential Code.

Division 09 00 00 Finishes

09 25 23 Lime-based plaster, including adobe floor

Natural finishes can be an impactful way to eliminate some of the most likely sources of Red List chemicals. Though more labor intensive, some projects in the Southwest have found adobe flooring to be a material that can provide a biophilic connection to the earth and to the context of the surrounding ecosystem. The Living Homes at Mill Creek installed both adobe floors,and as well as traditional plaster, which also avoids Red List chemicals that can be found in some gypsum wallboard products.

8 https://healthymaterialslab.org/projects/pa-hemp-home

2. Easy to Spec Red List Free

This level includes CSI sections that, unlike the previous level, are likely to include many products that contain Red List chemicals. However, the product types listed below can also be easily found Red List Free, with a small amount of research time, design effort, and minimal or no added costs. For ease of healthier product selection, standard specification should be updated to prioritize Red List Free options.

This level includes products under CSI Divisions 07 and 09.

Division 07 00 00 Thermal and Moisture Protection

Products in Division 7 are located inside of the waterproofing system with a significant impact on the indoor air quality and health of occupants. Many products in this section will also commonly contain Red List ingredients. Declare and the Affordable Housing Materials List includes many products in Division 7.

Insulation

07 21 00 Batt Insulation
07 21 00 Rigid Board Insulation

Many insulation products commonly contain several Red List chemicals such as halogenated flame retardants (HFR), formaldehyde, and phthalates.[9] HFRs are persistent bioaccumulative toxins that have been accumulating exponentially in humans in recent years. Formaldehyde is classified as a carcinogen and asthmagen. Phthalates are endocrine disruptors and cause harm to childhood development, reproductive system, and increase the incidence of cancer.[10] There are many Red List Free affordable product options available in Declare that are proven and durable products that are familiar to many affordable housing developers and architects. Affordable housing project teams have successfully specified Red List Free insulation products in many projects by manufacturers with Declare labels. There are nearly 50 insulation products with a Declare label as of March 2023.

Note that spray polyurethane foam products are not included on the Affordable Housing Materials List because spray foam will almost always contain Red List chemicals, such as halogenated flame retardants.[11] Batt, rigid board, acoustic, and blown-in insulations can generally be specified Red List Free using products with Declare labels (see the Affordable Housing Materials List for a list of dozens of products).

Photo: Eric McClean/Unsplash

9 assets.ctfassets.net/ntcn17sslow9/6lpUnRB2ABFvoBHtlhA7aY/fe4ccd5a4634c703495e33b811a411a1/NRDC-3094_Specifying_Healhier_Materials_report_05.pdf

10 living-future.org/red-list/

11 assets.ctfassets.net/ntcn17sslow9/6lpUnRB2ABFvoBHtlhA7aY/fe4ccd5a4634c703495e33b811a411a1/NRDC-3094_Specifying_Healhier_Materials_report_05.pdf

Vapor Barriers

07 26 00 Vapor Barriers

Vapor barriers are often made of high-density polyethylene, which should typically not contain Red List chemicals. There are several sheet-applied and fluid-applied products available with Declare labels. Affordable housing project teams have indicated that Declare-labeled vapor barrier products are widely available and economical. Note that vapor barriers may sometimes be made of PVC or extruded polystyrene boards, which typically contain HFRs.[12] PVC is on the Red List because its monomer, vinyl chloride is carcinogenic; it is also a Persistent Organic Pollutant Source Materials that often contains lead, phthalates, and cadmium (a very toxic heavy metal), and can result in the production of dioxins, some of the most potent toxins to humans with no safe limit for exposure.[13] The train derailment in East Palestine, Ohio in February 2023, posed a high likelihood to experts to have released dioxins into the surrounding community when vinyl chloride (the monomer for PVC) was burned.[14]
Division 09 00 00 Finishes
Similar to products in Division 7, finishes in Division 9 have a significant impact on the indoor air quality and health of occupants due to their location on the interior of the building and their large surface area.

Gypsum Board

09 29 00 Gypsum Board

Gypsum board is a relatively easy product type to specify Red List Free, as there are many compliant gypsum board products in Declare that should be cost-neutral products with proven performance and durability records. Wallboard products without Declare labels may contain traces of heavy metals, particularly synthetic gypsum, as byproducts of coal production.[15] Additionally, some gypsum products, especially those marked 'mold-resistant,' may contain antimicrobials[16] which are on the Red List due to their potential effects on hormones, learning, and muscle function. [17]

Ceramic Tile

09 30 00 Tile

There are many Red List Free tile products in Declare that are expected to be cost-neutral to other tiles products. Some affordable housing developers (such as Foundation Communities in Austin, Texas) have found that tile is a cost effective flooring option that requires little maintenance or replacement over time and also avoids the health and environmental issues associated with vinyl flooring. Tile products without Declare labels (or other forms of disclosure) may contain lead in the glaze or in added recycled content,[18] underlining why it is important to utilize products with transparency. Note also, as

12 healthybuilding.net/products/7-insulation

13 living-future.org/red-list/

14 www.statnews.com/2023/02/21/east-palestine-train-chemicals/

15 informed.healthybuilding.net/explore

16 informed.healthybuilding.net/explore

17 living-future.org/red-list/#red-list-and-watch-list-casrn-guide

18 informed.healthybuilding.net/explore#

stated under Division 12 36 00 countertops, sealers and grout may contain per- and polyfluorinated alkyl substances (PFAS) and should be vetted against the Red List. However, it is possible to find Red List Free grout and sealers and, one manufacturer, Drytile has even made a Declare-labeled product that eliminates the need for grout.

Acoustic Ceiling Tile and Acoustic Treatment

09 51 00 Acoustic Ceiling Tile
09 80 00 Acoustic Treatment

As of the publication of this document, there are dozens of acoustic ceiling tile products and suspension systems available in Declare from established manufacturers such as Armstrong World Industries and United States Gypsum. Project teams should be able to easily find Red List Free products with a Declare label. Acoustic ceiling tiles without Declare labels or product disclosure information may contain formaldehyde as binders or antimicrobials as coatings.

Carpet

09 68 00 Carpet
09 68 61 Sheet Carpeting
09 68 13 Tile Carpeting

There are many Red List Free affordable carpet options available with a Declare label. Standard carpet products will commonly include Red List ingredients, such as PVC, PFAS, antimicrobials, and HFRs.[19] Products marketed with stain repellant treatments are likely to contain PFAS. The existence of a Declare label makes the differentiation easier. To maintain healthy indoor environments, project teams should consider minimizing carpeted areas, which tend to harbor dust and allergens much more than other flooring options.

Paints and Coatings

09 90 00 Paint
09 61 00 Flooring Treatment (concrete floors)
09 93 00 Staining and Transparent Finishing

Interior wet-applied products, such as paint, are a critical product from a health impact standpoint. Paints and other coatings often contain high levels of volatile organic compounds (VOC), which will affect indoor air quality, and/or alkylphenol ethoxylates (APEs), which are endocrine disruptors. There are many Red List Free exterior and interior paint and coating products available on the market that should have minimal or no cost implications. Mineral paints are an option that are likely to avoid Red List Chemicals and the potential for microplastic pollution associated with acrylic latex paints.[20] Project teams should avoid epoxy coatings, as they usually contain bisphenol A (BPA), a reproductive and neurological toxin.

19 healthybuilding.net/products/1-flooring
20 architizer.com/blog/practice/materials/microplastic-plastic-paint-alternatives/

3. Some Cost Implications

This level includes product types that do have some Red List Free and affordable options, including options with Declare labels. Many project teams will already be using Red List Free options for several of these product types and, even teams not pursuing the Living Building Challenge, may be able to integrate Red List Free options for many, if not all of the others.

However, the products listed in this level may have some moderate cost premiums, and/or there may be fewer Red List Free products available than in the previous level. In some cases, such as resilient flooring, there are actually many Red List Free options available with Declare labels, from several different manufacturers. Many of these flooring options are reasonably priced and are often included in affordable housing project budgets. However, if a baseline of vinyl flooring is assumed, then any other options can tend to be somewhat more expensive. Note that product types like vinyl flooring externalize the negative impacts of their products. They often cause environmental degradation or otherwise negatively impact surrounding communities, letting them appear cheaper than if they bore the full responsibility for their impact. Vinyl flooring also has toxic maintenance protocols that can add to the long term costs of the product.

This level includes products in CSI Divisions 06 - 09, 12, and 22.

Division 06 00 00 Wood, Plastics, and Composites

Composite Wood

06 12 00 Structural Panels
06 15 00 Wood Decking
06 16 00 Sheathing (not GWB)
06 17 00 Shop fabricated structural wood (LVL, CLT)
06 20 00 Finish Carpentry, Millwork, Interior Architectural Woodwork
06 70 00 Structural Composites

Composite wood will often contain high amounts of formaldehyde and it is often better to use solid wood wherever possible to avoid Red List chemicals. Some manufacturers such as Columbia Forest Products, have successfully avoided added formaldehyde by producing plywood made with soy-based resins. Several formaldehyde-free products have Declare labels and have been included in affordable housing project team budgets for items such as casework. If Red List Free options cannot be found, particularly for casework or countertops, the Institute has issued a temporary Exception for the use of a very small amount of formaldehyde in composite wood based on the lack of available products on the market in the USA. The guidance, which can be found in the Petal Handbook, provides a pathway to mitigate the amount of formaldehyde used, while not avoiding its use entirely in this specific instance. Exceptions such as this are very limited in scope and considered temporary until the market evolves to remove Red List ingredients in these applications. Note also that, according to the Healthy Building Network, plywood has the least amount of formaldehyde-containing binder, by weight, (3.5%) and should be prioritized over MDF or particleboard, which have more than double this amount.[21] Per ILFI's exception, in LBC projects, plywood used for structural applications, such as sheathing, may contain added formaldehyde; plywood used for finished applications, it is imperative to prioritize FSC certified products in order to avoid contributing to deforestation.

Division 07 00 00 Thermal and Moisture Protection

Dampproofing/Waterproofing

07 10 00 Dampproofing + Waterproofing

Waterproofing membranes are often made of PVC. However, there are TPO, EPDM, and other sheet membrane products available in Declare. There are also multiple Red List Free fluid-applied products available with Declare labels and/or Health Product Declarations. Many of these options are likely to have minimal cost implications, but some may be more expensive than conventional PVC options.

Roofing and Siding

07 41 00 Metal Roof Panels
07 42 00 Wall Panels and Rainscreens
07 46 00 Siding
07 50 00 Membrane Roofing

Roofing and siding products are considered, for the purposes of this guide, to be moderately difficult because a baseline of PVC-based products is still used by some affordable housing developers, which will likely be cheaper than Red List Free options. However, there are many Red List Free options and many affordable housing developers have specified these products, even in very low-budget projects Several Red List Free TPO and EPDM roofing membranes are available in Declare, including a Red List Free TPO roofing system from GAF. Red List Free TPO roofing is a commonly used building product that has been specified by many affordable housing project teams; however, single-ply PVC roofing membranes are still used and TPO is likely to cost more than these options (though TPO roofing is becoming more cost competitive to PVC and is more energy-efficient, recyclable at end of life, and durable). Note also that EPDM membranes may contain halogenated flame retardants;[22] project teams not pursuing the Living Building Challenge should consider requesting product ingredient disclosure from the manufacturer if you are using a product without a Declare label. Wood, metal, and cementitious siding products can also be found Red List Free and are generally good options to avoid Red List chemicals, particularly in vinyl siding, though there is less product disclosure available for many cementitious siding products (however, the Affordable Housing Materials List currently lists Red List Free products from Cembrit). Ensure that wood, metal, or cementitious siding products utilize Red List Free coatings or paint, or use a wood material that does not require a sealer and embrace the aesthetic of natural weathering. Cementitious products will also have a higher embodied carbon footprint so this should be carefully considered as well.

21 informed.healthybuilding.net/explore

22 healthybuilding.net/products/13-roofing

Fireproofing
07 81 00 Applied Fireproofing
07 84 13 Penetration Firestopping
07 81 23 Intumescent Fireproofing
07 84 46 Fire-Resistive Joint Systems
07 82 00 Board Fireproofing

Fireproofing products will often contain multiple Red List ingredients, including halogenated flame retardants, formaldehyde, and BPA. Interior Sprayed Fire-Resistive Material (SFRM), spray applied plaster coating, gypsum, cementitious, and intumescent coating products can all be found Red List Free and several products are available in Declare from multiple manufacturers.

Division 08 00 00 Openings

Storefront
08 41 13 Storefront

Aluminum storefront systems will often contain PVC connectors. Red List Free options can be found on the market and in Declare, but these may pose a moderate cost increase over other options.

Division 09 00 00 Finishes

Resilient Flooring
09 65 00 Resilient Flooring

In lieu of vinyl flooring, project teams should consider linoleum or other bio-based flooring in applications where vinyl is typically specified. Linoleum can usually meet the performance requirements of a project and often proves more durable than vinyl flooring. There are many of these types of resilient flooring products with Declare labels. Although these have historically not been as affordable as vinyl-based flooring, this is starting to change, with some project teams reporting that PVC-free resilient flooring can be cost-neutral. Additionally, note that vinyl flooring contains PVC, phthalates, and other Red List ingredients, and the manufacturing of petroleum-derived products, such as PVC, causes detrimental impacts on neighboring communities, which are most often low-income and/or BIPOC communities.[23] Some affordable housing project teams have found polished concrete flooring to be an affordable and low-maintenance option for flooring in some areas (but remember to choose Red List Free sealers to avoid PFAS). In addition, vinyl wall base also contains PVC and project teams should consider specifying rubber, tile, or wood base products.

Division 12 00 00 Furnishings

Window Treatments
12 20 00 Window Treatment

Window treatments, particularly blinds, are often made of PVC and may also contain phthalates. Red List Free roller shade and aluminum blind options are available, several of which have Declare labels. However, they are likely to be somewhat more expensive, if the baseline product is PVC blinds. Project teams may also consider using smart glass options (at least one of which has a Declare label) that can help avoid using blinds.

23 informed.healthybuilding.net/explore

Casework

12 30 00 Casework (sometimes also listed under Division 06 00 00 Wood, Plastics, and Composites)

Select solid wood components for casework wherever possible to avoid Red List ingredients associated with composite wood materials (especially formaldehyde, a known carcinogen and asthmagen). To avoid Red List ingredients, leave wood products unfinished or carefully vet any paints, sealers, or coatings; there are several Red List Free options on the Affordable Housing Materials List and in Declare. Project teams should also prioritize sourcing FSC certified wood products in order to avoid detrimental environmental effects associated with deforestation. Note that FSC certified casework products may be harder to source and/or may cost more, but this varies widely regionally. In some areas, FSC certified casework products have a minimal or no cost premium, but FSC framing products can be much more expensive than conventional alternatives and in some regions, the inverse is true (and in some regions, there is a minimal or no cost increase for either type of FSC wood).

Countertops

12 36 00 Countertops

Several Red List Free or Approved quartz and solid surface countertops are available in Declare, many of which are options that can be integrated into affordable housing budgets. Mineral or stone-based countertops do not need to be sealed after installation and avoid Red List ingredients that may be present in sealers. However, these may be somewhat more expensive than laminate countertop options, which are likely to contain PVC or formaldehyde. As mentioned, one project team installed concrete countertops as a creative way to avoid Red List chemicals. Note that sealers for concrete (and for countertops) often contain Red List ingredients, but you can find Red List Free options in Declare.

Division 22 00 00 Plumbing

Plumbing fixtures

22 40 00 Plumbing Fixtures

There are many Red List Free plumbing fixtures listed in the Declare database, including water closets, urinals, lavatories, kitchen sinks, and faucets. Fixtures with Declare labels are typically high-performance and should help reduce water use in the building as well. Bathroom accessories such as towel and grab bars can also be found in Declare. Note that plumbing fixtures, especially those with a chrome finish, may contain hexavalent chromium (Chromium VI), a toxic heavy metal on the Red List due to its link to breathing problems and certain cancers.[24] Project teams should request product disclosures for all products or use products with Declare labels to avoid this. Additionally, note that, as of the date of this publication, Chromium VI will most likely not be avoidable in the plating on flush levers and commercial flush valves due to a lack of alternative materials available for this application (LBC project teams will follow the relevant Exception regarding this application in the Living Building Challenge Materials Petal Handbook). All project teams should also ensure that all plumbing fixtures meet the

24 living-future.org/red-list/

federal definition of "lead free,"as defined in S. 3874 (111th): Reduction of Lead in Drinking Water Act, effective January 1, 2014; however, most reputable manufacturers will meet this standard. Affordable housing project teams have encountered difficulty finding bath and shower surrounds with an appropriate level of disclosure to determine whether they contain Red List ingredients. At this time it is not clear if acrylic or other bath and shower surrounds typically used in affordable housing buildings would contain Red List chemicals. Several project teams have used tile to avoid this issue; as mentioned above, there are many compliant ceramic tiles products.

Piping

22 10 00 Plumbing Piping and Pumps

Some types of plumbing piping (such as sprinkler piping and sometimes domestic water systems) are commonly made with PVC or CPVC (which is in the same chemical class as PVC). Copper, PEX (crosslinked polyethylene), HPDE, steel, polypropylene, and cast iron are also common options, all of which will most likely not contain Red List chemicals; however, note that copper piping joined with solder may contain lead and should be avoided. There are several cast iron pipes with Declare labels. Several manufacturers have Declare labels for cast iron pipe products; however, cast iron pipes are likely to be more expensive than PVC piping.

4. Limited Options with Cost Implications

The Institute has consistently received feedback that the product types listed below tend to be challenging for affordable housing project teams. This does not mean that there are no options and it does not mean that affordable housing project teams cannot specify Red List Free products in the sections below. There are several options for all of these categories within Declare and listed on the Affordable Housing Materials List. However, some of these product types will typically be more expensive and sometimes significantly more expensive than baseline options. Some product types are not necessarily more expensive, but may have limited Red List Free options. The products in this level are prime for collective research and advocacy; by more teams participating in the effort to specify Red List Free products, more manufacturers will be pushed to create Red List Free products as well as provide transparency and pursue Declare labels.

It is helpful to ensure that the entire project team is a part of all sustainability goals, including healthy materials, from the beginning. Contractors could be recruited to help find acceptable products for this section, since many of them are likely to be more familiar with the performance and installation properties. They also may be invested in finding products that are also safer for them and their teams, since they are in direct contact with the products on a daily basis. Project teams can also creatively balance the budget to include Red List Free options that do have a cost increase. Teams in the past have reduced parking

(that was not needed) and been selective about adding balconies only on sides of the building where they were likely to be utilized and not on units facing busy streets.
This level includes products in CSI Divisions 07 and 08.

Division 07 00 00 Thermal and Moisture Protection

Adhesives and Sealants

07 90 00 Adhesives and sealants
09 30 13 Mortar + Grout

There are adhesives and sealants with Declare labels. Products without Declare labels are likely to include Red List chemicals (including phthalates and VOCs). As wet-applied products, these off-gas (release chemicals into the air) upon installation and impact the health of installers and residents. Project teams should prioritize using adhesives and sealants with Declare labels and try to minimize the use of these products overall throughout the building by relying on mechanical installation methods or products that do not require adhesives. For example, one manufacturer has a Red List Free tile product that requires no adhesives for installation.

Healthy Building Network's Informed tool provides guidance on which product types, including sealants, are likely to be healthier options; in general, products ranked yellow and green are likely to be Red List Free products while products ranked red are likely to contain Red List ingredients. In addition, product types ranked yellow and green minimize the use of hazardous chemicals throughout the product's life cycle (manufacturing, installation, maintenance, and end of life), which disproportionately impact people of color, low-wealth populations, and children. Project teams can use this guidance to direct their research efforts toward products that are most likely to be Red List Free.

Division 08 00 00 Openings

Doors

08 11 00 Metal Doors
08 33 00 Overhead + Coiling Doors
08 14 00 Wood Doors
08 70 00 Door Hardware

It can be difficult to find Red List Free doors suitable for use on multi-family residential projects. Doors are often made of composite wood and contain high levels of formaldehyde. Red List Free wood doors are available that have been specified on affordable housing projects by prioritizing them in the budget, but may carry a cost premium. As an alternative, metal doors can be found Red List Free; several manufacturers have Declare labels and these will often not have Red List ingredients. Overhead coiling doors can also likely be found Red List Free. Door hardware can be found Red List Free and there are multiple options in Declare.

Windows

08 50 00 Windows

There are more Red List Free windows available in Declare than in the past; however, PVC or uPVC windows are, unfortunately, likely to be the cheapest option available and tend to be ubiquitous in affordable housing projects. Note that uPVC does not contain plasticizers, but still includes other Red List chemicals in the manufacturing process. Some wood windows may contain engineered wood components with formaldehyde and may not fit into the budget for affordable housing projects. There are fiberglass and aluminum windows with Declare labels, but these are also likely to have a price premium compared to vinyl windows. However, some affordable housing project teams have been able to fit fiberglass windows into the budget by prioritizing it. Affordable housing project teams, particularly non-profits, should also consider reaching out to manufacturers of Red List Free options to request discounts.

5. Few Options/Request Transparency

This level includes product types where there are likely to be few, if any, Red List Free options available. Most of the products under these CSI sections are complex equipment and it can be challenging to find complete disclosures that include all components of the product. If a team is limited on research time, the products in this level should be a lower priority; for Living Building Challenge project teams these product types often use a General Red List Exception and/or are part of the 10% that is excluded from the Red List scope. As for all products, asking manufacturers for transparency is a crucial first step to impact change in these product categories. Many of the products in this level will have significant impacts on energy efficiency and water use and these concerns may be a primary driver for product selection.

This level includes products in CSI Divisions 14, 22, 23, and 26.

Division 14 00 00 Conveying Equipment

14 20 00 Elevators

There are limited options for Red List Free options, although one manufacturer does have two elevator cabins with Declare labels. Refer to the section on electrical equipment below for the Institute's approach to vetting electrical equipment.

Division 22 00 00 Plumbing

22 30 00 Plumbing Equipment

Domestic hot water heaters are complex equipment as well and it may be difficult to find Red List Free options, due to the number of components that need to be disclosed. Many affordable housing project teams have reported that domestic hot water systems are one of the top uses of energy in the project so specifying efficient fixtures to reduce operational energy should be a focus. Note also that natural gas hot water heaters can be common in affordable housing (though prohibited by all ILFI building certifications), depending on the region, and specifying electrical equipment should be a goal both to decarbonize the built environment and to eliminate health hazards associated with gas equipment. A study completed by one affordable housing pilot project team found that substituting a CO2 heat pump hot water system reduced energy use associated with domestic hot water by 70%.

Division 23 00 00 Heating, Ventilation, and Air Conditioning

23 00 00 Heating, Ventilation, and Air Conditioning

Manufacturers of HVAC equipment often have difficulty providing transparency information due to the complex nature of their products and complicated supply chains. For Living Building Challenge projects teams, the Institute has an Exception that allows project teams to exclude small components that are less than 10%, by weight, of the product. This Exception was created to allow project teams to focus efforts and not become stymied by an inability to find documentation for every single minor component of each piece of equipment, which can be challenging. Project teams should request transparency for these products, but also balance the effort and time that is allotted to each individual product or CSI section.

Division 26 00 00 Electrical

26 00 00 Electrical
26 50 00 Lighting Fixtures
26 51 15 Ceiling Fans

There are many Red List Free lighting fixtures available with Declare labels. Finding other Red List Free and Declare-labeled electrical fixtures and equipment can be challenging. For example, ILFI is not aware of any Red List Free ceiling fans, as of this publication. Living Building Challenge project teams will use an Exception for products with small electrical components. LBC teams look for products that comply with the regulations of the European Union's Restriction of the Use of Certain Hazardous Substances (RoHS) Directive 3, 2015, which establishes maximum concentration values for toxic chemicals tolerated by weight in homogeneous materials, as mapped out in the Materials Petal Handbook.

6. Eliminate

The products in the level below will always contain Red List chemicals because these chemicals are an integral part of the product, such as in the case of vinyl flooring. Eliminate these products from standard specifications and design them out of projects as much as possible. These products can be replaced with Red List Free products from categories 1-4.

This level includes products in CSI Divisions 07 and 09.

Division 07 00 00 Thermal and Moisture Protection
07 21 13 Expanded Polystyrene (EPS) or Extruded Polystyrene (XPS) Insulation
07 21 19 Foamed In Place Insulation

The products above will almost always contain halogenated flame retardants (HFRs), which are persistent bioaccumulative toxins that have multiple impacts on human health. The manufacturing of these product types, particularly foamed in place insulation, also tends to contribute to significant pollution over its life cycle.25 The Living Building Challenge includes a limited Exception for LBC teams that allows for the use of HFRs in foam insulation, however, it is limited to very specific applications with limited space where no other product is acceptable. In most situations, project teams should strive to eliminate these products from their specifications and use an alternative insulation product (refer to the Affordable Housing Materials List for dozens of Red List Free insulation products!)

Division 09 00 00 Finishes
09 65 19 Vinyl Flooring

There are many better and Red List Free alternatives to vinyl flooring (including linoleum, which is unlikely to contain Red List chemicals). The Affordable Housing Materials List and Declare have dozens of options of Red List Free resilient flooring products. Though many affordable housing developers have stopped using vinyl flooring, it is still used widely.

All other vinyl-based products
It is important to keep in mind that the production of vinyl chloride produces many negative environmental effects, which have been externalized by the industry, and are largely borne by disadvantaged frontline communities, as was witnessed in the February 2023 train derailment and chemical spill in East Palestine, Ohio. No vinyl is the best option.

25 healthybuilding.net/reports/24-chemical-and-environmental-justice-impacts-in-the-life-cycle-of-building-insulation

GETTING STARTED: SETTING GOALS AND GENERAL GUIDANCE

A Path to Red List Free Materials for Affordable Housing

The market for Red List Free materials began to shift when project teams demanded that manufacturers provide transparency and also shift their product chemistry to exclude harmful chemicals. Declare now has grown to include thousands of products. With a concerted effort of manufacturers, project teams, and organizations like the International Living Future Institute, Healthy Building Network, Energy Efficiency for All, Toxic-Free Future, Green Science Policy Institute, Parsons Healthy Materials Lab, and others, industries have shifted in significant ways — for example, phthalates, which cause impacts on childhood and reproductive development, have mostly been eliminated in flooring products (though PVC, which contains several carcinogenic process chemicals, is still often present).
The previous chapter includes six levels of products: 1) Typically Red List Free, 2) Easy to Spec Red List Free, 3) Some Cost Implications, 4) Limited Options with Cost Implications, 5) Few Options/Request Transparency, and 6) Eliminate. To begin the journey to Red List Free affordable housing, ILFI suggests that each team set specific goals that includes most (if not all) products that can be easily integrated while pushing to research, implement, and advocate for at least a few products that are more of a reach. The six levels are not definitive and may change over time as both the Red List and the product market evolves. The delineations are not intended to dissuade project team members from attempting to find Red List Free products in the more challenging areas, but to have a realistic understanding of available options and to help funnel time and effort into products that are likely to have the most success and to encourage advocacy for the product types that have limited options.

Below are a few suggested goals that project teams could set to begin incorporating Red List Free products and creating healthier homes. Project teams should begin by taking inventory of where they are in the process of healthy materials. You can use the Affordable Housing Materials List to quickly review each CSI division and highlight products that are commonly specified. When you review the products in the standard specifications against this list, you may realize that you already use many Red List Free products, particularly from Levels 1 and 2. Project teams may be ready for different goals, depending on their starting point. Some project teams may want to begin with Step 1, while others may be ready for Step 5. Any of the goals below could be starting points; ILFI's Affordable Housing Project Teams in the past have chosen goals from each level (even completely Red List Free!) for their projects. Project teams should strive to build upon successes and pursue higher percentages of Red List Free materials with each project. Note, however, that the goals below do not have to necessarily be pursued in order. Project teams may find after pursuing Step 1 on an initial project that they can leapfrog to Step 4.

Photo: Sven Mieke/Unsplash

Pursuing one of the goals below will help project teams to start engaging with Red List Free products and view each project as an opportunity to eliminate as many Red List chemicals as possible, as well as a chance to advocate. The more teams that begin taking on specifying Red List Free products and asking manufacturers and other team members about them, the quicker the market will move and the easier it will be for everyone to build Red List Free Affordable Housing.

Example Steps to Red List Free

1. **Incorporate Red List free materials for all Level 1 and 2 products into every project.**
   This should be an easy step for most teams.

2. **All level 1 and 2 products are Red List Free/Approved +**
   Choose 5 individual products from level 3 or 4 to research and reserve in budget.
   Advocate to manufacturers of Level 5 products.

3. **All Level 1 and 2 products are Red List Free/Approved +**
   Choose 10 individual products from level 3 or 4 to research and reserve in budget.
   Advocate to manufacturers of Level 5 products.

4. **All Level 1 and 2 products are Red List Free/Approved +**
   Choose 2 CSI sections from level 3 or 4 to research and reserve in budget.
   Advocate to manufacturers of Level 5 products.

5. **All Level 1 and 2 products are Red List Free/Approved +**
   Choose 4 CSI sections from level 3 or 4 to research and reserve in budget.
   Advocate to manufacturers of Level 5 products.

6. **All interior finish materials are Red List Free/Approved.**

7. **All Level 1-4 products are Red List Free/Approved.**
   Advocate to manufacturers of Level 5 products.
   Eliminate all Level 6 products.

8. **90% of products are Red List Free/ Approved. Where it is not possible to find Red List Free/Approved products, advocate to the manufacturer.**
   Note that this step is in line with the Living Building Challenge Materials Petal requirements for the Red List. (Living Building Challenge projects are subject to additional requirements regarding materials in the Materials, Health + Happiness, and Energy Petals.)

STRATEGIES FOR INTEGRATING HEALTHY MATERIALS

As you strive toward LBC certification or one of the goals above, remember that you are not alone in the pursuit of Red List Free products! Many LBC project teams have embarked on this quest and have useful lessons and strategies to pass along. The tips below can help assist you in being successful.

Use unfinished, uncoated products

Products such as adhesives, sealants, and sealers often have Red List chemicals. If you can embrace a raw aesthetic or use materials that do not require additional coatings, you can avoid many of these chemicals. Many products, such as wood and concrete, are Red List Free, but introduce Red List chemicals when they are coated or treated. Some products may naturally weawther over time in a way that does not affect durability. It is worth challenging assumptions about aesthetics to prioritize the health of occupants and communities.

Integrate natural products

Some affordable housing project teams, most notably the Living Homes at Mill Creek, have utilized many natural products, such as adobe floors and straw bale insulation, which helped them avoid Red List chemicals and build in a contextual, climate-appropriate way. Natural materials were used successfully by indigenous communities for hundreds of years and many have excellent performance attributes without introducing Red List chemicals into the space or supply chain.

Avoid plastic as much as possible

Plastic-containing products very often contain PVC, phthalates, or other Red List chemicals. Prioritizing using wood, linoleum, stone, or other non-plastic materials wherever feasible will help to eliminate this issue. Plastics are petroleum-derived products and frequently contain chemicals that are linked to chronic health issues, whether they directly pose a risk to occupants or to someone else in the supply chain.[26] For more information on how the ubiquity of plastic products is undermining our collective attempts at decarbonization and externalizing costs to BIPOC and low-income communities, read *Our Plastic Buildings — the New Driver of Fossil Fuel Demand* from the Healthy Building Network's July 2021 Newsletter.

Streamline the materials palette

This is a best practice to avoid unnecessary embodied carbon and Red List chemicals. A minimalist aesthetic focuses research time on the needed materials and saves cost. Aside from finishes, eliminating wet-applied products such as adhesives in favor of mechanical installation methods reduces likely sources of Red List chemicals. Strategically reduce the amount of materialS Utilizing standardized floor plans, right-sizing wall dimensions to reduce drywall, and other Lean construction practices can reduce waste and significantly reduce materials costs, which can allow room in the budget for Red List Free or Approved products that may have a cost premium.[27]

26 Reference: Landrigan PJ, Raps H, Cropper M, Bald C, Brunner M, Canonizado EM, et al. The Minderoo-Monaco Commission on Plastics and Human Health. Ann Glob Heal [Internet]. 2023 Mar 21;89(1):1-215. Available from: annalsofglobalhealth.org/articles/10.5334/aogh.4056/

27 www.walshconstruction.com/2022/06/exploring-a-different-path-to-more-better-housing/

Coliseum Place, Oakland, CA. Image courtesy of David Baker Architects.

Think about the project and budget holistically
Can other elements in the building be reduced or eliminated to facilitate incorporation of healthy materials? Could parking be reduced? Are there other building elements that are unnecessary or unlikely to be utilized? Consider the project priorities carefully and be creative if value engineering is necessary.

Focus research time on product types most likely to have Red List Free options
The guidance in Chapter 3 provides information on which products currently have the most Red List Free options. Rather than taking on the most difficult products first, it is advisable to start accumulating wins on as many products as possible and, especially if research time is limited, direct efforts where you are most likely to succeed. LBC project teams may also find it useful to begin research on the easier products first.

Recruit contractors and construction teams to help
Contractors will be critical to the success of a healthy materials goal. Include LBC or healthy materials goals in your Request for Proposals (RFP) to ensure that you find partners that share your commitment. Contractors have deep knowledge about installation properties of products, such as adhesives and, as day-to-day users of the product, are most likely to be affected by health impacts. Integrated design processes and delineating a clear role and process for each member of the team is critical to success.

Work with manufacturers and think creatively
Affordable housing projects are typically built by mission-driven and non-profit developers. It is worth asking manufacturers if they can donate or reduce costs of materials in order to help your team create a healthier building in communities where it is greatly needed. Manufacturers may be able to brainstorm creative solutions to decrease the costs. For example, one manufacturer suggested aligning the production of their material to the factory's slow periods, in order to allow them to offer it at a lower price to an affordable housing project team — a win for both parties.

CONCLUSION

The International Living Future Institute envisions a future where the built environment is free of chemicals that have the potential to cause harm to those manufacturing the product, installers and construction workers, building occupants, and those that may dispose of a product at the end of its life. We especially envision this future for the low-income and BIPOC communities that have borne the brunt of some of our country's worst policies and environmental disasters. They have often been the frontline communities that have had to breathe hazards in the air and live with substandard building materials in their homes. They have often been the first ones to begin to experience the impacts of climate change. The health of underserved communities must be prioritized in our collective action for healthier spaces and avoiding harmful chemicals. The affordable housing project teams that ILFI has worked with over the past decade have begun to show that it is possible to begin eliminating Red List Free chemicals in affordable housing. It is time for the sector to join together to prioritize the health of residents and communities and to chart a Path to Red List Free Materials for Affordable Housing together.

**Hunter's View Phase III, San Francisco, CA.
Rendering courtesy of David Baker Architects**

Appendix A: Resources

- **ILFI Affordable Housing and Materials Resources:**
  - Affordable Housing Materials List: A downloaded spreadsheet of Red List Free products, by CSI division.
  - "Ask" Templates: Sample letters to send manufacturers to request disclosure of product ingredients.
  - Materials Case Studies: Three case studies of affordable housing project teams pursuing the Living Building Challenge, including a list of Red List Free products that were specified.
  - Building Product Selection Guidance: This guide provides an overview of the materials requirements in the Living Building Challenge (LBC) 4.0 Materials Petal compliance, as well as key strategies and tips.
  - Sample specifications: Template specifications for project teams to reference when including Red List requirements in their Construction Documents.
- **Declare:** Declare is a nutrition label for building products. Declare labels disclose all intentionally-added ingredients and residuals at or above 100 ppm (0.01%) present in the final product by weight.
- **Living Building Challenge Petal Handbooks:** The Petal Handbooks are available for free to all active Living Future members. The Petal Handbooks provide additional guidance and pathways for all seven petals, including the Materials Petal.
- **Parsons Healthy Materials Lab:** The Lab offers educational resources including online courses, practice guidance, and tools to select healthier materials for affordable housing. They have also created materials collections of common building products and low embodied carbon materials. The collections include information for all products that have Declare labels, HPD's, EPD's and other Material Health and Embodied Carbon related certifications and note any products that have been used in affordable housing.
- **Healthy Building Network's Informed:** Informed is a new, simple materials modeling tool created by Healthy Building Network to help project teams select safer building products. Informed uses a straightforward color-based system to rank product types based on their chemical impacts over their life cycle. This approach gives project teams visual cues that make it easier to avoid the most hazardous products (ranked red and orange) and select safer options (ranked yellow and green). In addition, Informed provides key guidance to help project teams understand and communicate the rationale behind their product choices. By avoiding product types ranked red, and choosing product types that are ranked yellow and green, project teams will typically select products that are free of Red List Chemicals. In addition to avoiding Red List chemicals in the product, product types ranked yellow and green minimize the use of hazardous chemicals throughout the

product's life cycle (manufacturing, installation, maintenance, and end of life), which disproportionately impact people of color, low-wealth populations, and children. Leveraging a materials modeling tool like Informed can help project teams identify chemical "hot spots" in their buildings, create benchmarks, set goals, and illustrate and communicate findings to other stakeholders. Data can be used to calculate the weight or volume of hazardous chemicals avoided in a space, a room, or even a portfolio of projects.

- **Health Product Declaration Collaborative:** HPDC includes a repository of freely accessible health product declarations that report on product contents and health information, including identifying Red List chemicals.
- **Grace Farms Design for Freedom Toolkit:** A comprehensive resource for design and construction professionals to implement ethical, forced-labor free materials sourcing strategies into their practices. The Toolkit is organized into three areas of focus: Education, Commitment, and Implementation.
- **Energy Efficiency for All's Healthy Affordable Building Materials Initiative:** This initiative provides information on specifying healthier materials for multi-family energy efficiency upgrade and retrofit programs, particularly related to insulation and air sealing materials. Detailed reports can be downloaded from the website to assist in choosing the most preferable and healthy materials in these categories.
- **Toxic Free Future:** Toxic Free Future's website includes research and investigative reports to bring environmental health issues to light.
- **Mindful Materials Common Materials Framework:** A database aggregating 100 most common product certifications (include Declare and the Living Building Challenge) with 650 sustainability factors in 5 broad buckets of health and sustainability.

INTERNATIONAL LIVING FUTURE INSTITUTE

The International Living Future Institute's mission is to cultivate a society that is socially just, culturally rich, and ecologically restorative. To do this, we envision a Living Future and show that it works better in practice and policy. With partners, this means aiming for regenerative communities, buildings, and products, rather than incremental improvements, to make progress much faster and in more transformational ways.

Now more than ever, we need a community working towards a common vision to make progress on the biggest challenges of our time: climate change, health, and justice. And the only path to a regenerative future has justice at its core, because if we aim for sustainability without also seeking justice, we sustain injustice.

The Institute has served as an incubator for more than 500 regenerative buildings around the country, showing what's possible. Now it's time to move past individual projects to coalesce around holistic policy reform at the community scale. A regenerative future in the Anthropocene Era is built on the premise that people are part of nature. When we recognize our place within nature, we create solutions that are efficient, resilient, and refined.

ECOTONE PUBLISHING

Ecotone Publishing is the non-profit publishing arm of the International Living Future Institute and a key component of the organization's Communication strategy for sharing expert information about green building technologies, materials, and design innovations to create a Living Future. As a publisher, Ecotone produces educational case studies, technical knowledge on renewable energy, plus regenerative and biophilic design, and is the leading source of published information about Living Buildings worldwide. Ecotone also offers professional publishing services to help design firms and organizations document and share their stories, lessons learned, industry reports, and design solutions with others who are also seeking to address the climate crisis and have a positive impact on their communities.

Proceeds from publications and reports re-circulate to support and renew the programs, research, education, and advocacy of the ILFI non-profit organization.